Confident Choices:

A Cookbook for Interstitial Cystitis and Overactive Bladder

Julie Beyer, MA, RD
NutraConsults, LLC

Confident Choices: A Cookbook for Interstitial Cystitis and Overactive Bladder
ISBN: 0976724626
First Printing

Published in the United States of America by:

NutraConsults, LLC
P.O. Box 210086, Auburn Hills, MI 48321
www.NutraConsults.com

To order a copy of this book, please visit:
www.nutraconsults.com/confidentchoices.html

Disclaimer: Confident Choices, a division of NutraConsults, LLC, is not a medical authority. No information written or implied in this cookbook, the Confident Choices website, the Confident Choices newsletter, or any resource recommended should be considered medical advice. Please contact your physician for information regarding any change you wish to make in your lifestyle. Confident Choices urges you to carefully research ANY information that you find regarding health and wellness, including information received from NutraConsults. **Trademark notice:** This book uses various trademarked names within its text. In the interest of the reader, we are using the trademarked names in an editorial style. In the interest of the trademark holders, we cite their ownership of the trademarks, with no intention of infringement. **Recipe copyrights:** This book is a collection that not only includes recipes submitted by readers, family and friends, but recipes used with permission from various companies and websites. All copyrights were acknowledged whenever they were known to exist. If any recipe or reference needs to be updated, please send updated information to NutraConsults@aol.com. Changes will be made in subsequent printings.

Time sensitive materials: At the time of publication, all names, addresses, telephone numbers, email and Web addresses were verified as accurate.

♥ *Dedication* ♥

To all of the generous interstitial cystitis patients who graciously shared their experience and wisdom with me over the past ten years.

This book is my way of paying it forward.

Acknowledgements

The publication of a book is a journey. For the past ten years, interstitial cystitis (IC) patients and support group leaders have been urging me to write this book. *"After all,"* they would say, *"you are a dietitian AND you have IC. Who knows better than you?"*

They had no idea how inadequate I felt for the job. Just like many newly diagnosed IC patients, I was depressed, frustrated, and scared. I had no intention of putting myself out there as an "expert" when I was still struggling to sort it all out for myself.

Now when I look back, I realize that God had a plan for this project that I never could have mapped out for myself. Right when I needed it, He put people in my path to teach, mentor, and encourage me. Eventually the lessons, skills, and—most importantly—the moments of inspiration I experienced along the way converged to become my first book, *Confident Choices: Customizing the Interstitial Cystitis Diet.*

Today, when I look at that first book and the one you now hold in your hands, I can easily identify bits and pieces of the souls whose patience, wisdom, and friendship became the milestones of this journey:

Anton Anderssen, JD—teacher and confidant: Anton, you were the first person who introduced me to the world of self-publishing in 2000. Your enthusiasm and genuine love for life are contagious and continually inspire me—your unwavering support and friendship paved the way for these books to go from concept to reality.

Dina Aronson, MS, RD—mentor and friend: Dina, you were SO patient with me as you edited some of my first work back in 2001. Like a first-rate driving instructor, your gentle guidance kept me between the lines without scaring me away from the task. If that wasn't enough, in a situation where many people would have jealously guarded their business "secrets," you generously opened your heart and shared your experience as a nutrition communicator and entrepreneur. You are a joy to know and a friend for life.

Diana Dyer, MS, RD—inspiration and virtual teacher: Diana, reading your book, *A Dietitian's Cancer Story,* gave me the confidence to share my own story more intimately with my readers. What you may not know is that the first pages of *Confident Choices: Customizing the Interstitial Cystitis Diet* were written within hours of listening to the CD recording of your 2004 American Dietetic Association conference (FNCE) presentation "Nutrition Writing as a Career." Your inspiration was the bridge I needed to go from an "aspiring" to a "published" author.

Linda Schuessler, MS, RD—risk taker and champion of our profession: My dear Linda, I am humbled and grateful that you took a chance on me back in 2005. When you hired me to work with you on the wellness initiative at Fiserv, you provided me with a forum where I could continue to develop my communication and technology skills—skills that served me well in this second attempt at authorship. Thank you for taking time out of your retirement to share your editing talents. I could not have asked for a better companion on this leg of the journey.

Finally, there are those who have been with me every day and every night from the beginning. Authors rarely schedule their work from 9 to 5; rather, as many other writers will attest, the middle of the night seems to yield our best work. *Jim, Rebekah, Chi, Carolyn, and Daniel*—thank you for your patience and for allowing me the time and space to write this book. In addition, I want to express my genuine appreciation for *Jim's* keen eye for detail and *Carolyn's* English degree. This book would not be the same without them.

Contents

Introduction

     A good portion of writing a book is the "thinking" that happens during the months and even years prior to publication. It was very important to me that the content of this book actually addressed the needs of the readers. As you can imagine, the people I spoke with had some very specific ideas about what they did and did not want to see in a cookbook for bladder patients. Eventually, these conversations evolved into a kind of mission statement for *Confident Choices: A Cookbook for Interstitial Cystitis and Overactive Bladder.* I hope to outline some of that here.

     First, this book shouldn't be seen as a replacement for *Confident Choices: Customizing the Interstitial Cystitis Diet*, but rather a companion. Although I have included some meal planning hints from the previous book and an abbreviated version of the interstitial cystitis (IC) elimination diet in the appendix, you will find much more about actually implementing the process in *Confident Choices: Customizing the Interstitial Cystitis Diet* than you will here. You will also find valuable information about other lifestyle changes you can make including stress management and exercise modification strategies.

     The feedback that I received from IC patients after publishing that first book was incredibly positive, and the readers were asking for more. They wanted more recipes—recipes that were not complicated, recipes that didn't require unusual ingredients, and recipes to replace foods that they may have to avoid with IC. The recipes they asked for included salad dressings, homemade breads, snack foods, desserts and candies, and nutritious, bladder-safe main dishes that wouldn't require them to stand on their feet for hours, or consume all of their energy to prepare. For the record, I did not create all of these recipes myself. Instead, I took the recipes I had and supplemented them with recipes that I collected from other recipe authors. This book brings all of that into one place for you, so that you don't have to do the searching yourself when you don't feel well. I hope that the collection of recipes in *Confident Choices: A Cookbook for Interstitial Cystitis and Overactive Bladder* meets your expectations.

You will note that I included overactive bladder (OAB) patients as part of the audience for this cookbook. I did this for a couple of reasons. One, most of the foods that are troublesome for IC patients can also increase the symptoms of OAB. I have also talked to OAB patients who were frustrated when they were simply given medications and not given any education in the way of lifestyle changes that could help ease some of their symptoms. I hope, in a small way, that I can help educate some of these patients.

Aside from providing patients with a collection of "safe" recipes, it was important to me that this book would provide hope to people with IC and OAB. If you are a patient, it may seem to you that you will never lead a normal life again, but believe me, you will. If you think about it, nobody's life stays the same day to day anyway. People get married, have children, change jobs, and change homes. A normal life is always in flux. Try to think of the lifestyle changes you need to make as just a step in your journey. One of the best things you can do for yourself is to envision each problem you may face as an opportunity for positive change. You may not have chosen to have a chronic condition, but you do have it within your control to make lifestyle choices that can make your days and nights a little easier.

Finally, please feel free to contact me with your questions, comments, and even suggestions for future editions. I get some of my best ideas from other IC patients. Of course, I am always looking for new recipes. I am also available for individual counseling via the phone and for presentations at your local interstitial cystitis support group. To learn more visit www.NutraConsults.com/confidentchoices.html or send me an email at NutraConsults@aol.com.

Meal Planning

Planning your meals ahead of time and making a weekly grocery list based on that plan can help you eat healthier, keep you on track with bladder-friendly foods, and reduce mealtime frustration. Taking the time to plan meals can also increase satisfaction with your meals, despite the dietary limitations of a modified diet.

Good Nutrition with IC and OAB

There certainly are concerns about consuming healthy foods anytime your diet is restricted. Some people even turn to comfort foods when they are ill, rationalizing that they are sick anyway, so why does it matter what they eat? Many others, however, find that having to modify their diet for a particular health condition causes them to consider eating better than they had before their illness.

The first rule of good nutrition, even with dietary restrictions, is to eat a wide variety of foods. You can use the list on page 14 to guide your food choices.

Food Groups for Healthy Eating

Food Group	# Per Day	Serving Sizes
Dairy	2-3	1 c. low-fat milk 1 c. yogurt (if tolerated) 1 ½ oz. low-fat soft cheese
Fruits	3-4	1 medium pear 2 canned pear halves 3/4 c. fresh blueberries 1/2 c. frozen blueberries 1/4 c. dried dates without preservatives
Vegetables	3-5	1/2 c. cooked 1 c. raw, or salad
Grains	5-8	1 slice bread 1/2 c. dry or hot cereal 1/2 c. cooked rice or pasta
Meats/Protein	3 or less	2 to 3 oz. meat, poultry, fish 1-2 eggs 1/2 c. legumes
Nuts/Seeds	4 per week	1/3 c. nuts 2 T. seeds
Sweets/fats	limited	olive oil peanut oil canola oil sugar, brown sugar honey maple syrup

Keeping It Simple

If you are just beginning to use an elimination diet to determine your food triggers (see Appendix A, page 148), you can design menus using your "Usually OK" food list. It is also important to keep your meals as plain and simple as possible. It is much harder to filter out which food is causing your symptoms to flare if you are eating foods with many ingredients such as casseroles, soups, or stir-fries. Other hints for keeping it simple at this stage include:

- Make menu planning a family affair—consulting with other family members about menu choices can increase their understanding of your condition.

- Consider including foods that might be triggers for you, but that your family can eat—it was nearly a year before I realized that I had not been buying strawberries for my family just because I couldn't have them!

- Plan your snacks like you plan your meals. Choose foods with high nutritional value like carrots, cottage cheese, and homemade muffins.

- Create a grocery list from your menus and stick to your grocery list. A list insures that you have all the ingredients that you need for the week and helps prevent impulse buying, which can be tough on the wallet. (See Appendix C, page 169 for a sample grocery list.)

- Recycle your weekly meal plans like hospitals, cafeterias, and schools do to simplify planning. Once you have developed a few weeks of menus that you and your family enjoy, go ahead and reuse them. Save the grocery lists, too!

- Make two batches of a meal and freeze one for later. Everyone has days when they are too busy or too tired to cook. It is nice to have something available that you can quickly reheat.

- Involve everyone in mealtime activities. Establish this as a special time to spend with individual family members. Assign days when each person has a chance to help with breakfast or dinner. Even small children can help to set the table, measure ingredients, or stir batter.

- Simplify cleanup. Use disposable plates and utensils on days when symptoms flare or energy is limited. Line baking dishes with aluminum foil or bake food in foil pockets. Use a slow cooker with a disposable liner to bake a one pot, complete meal of meat, potatoes, and vegetables.

Abbreviations Used in this Cookbook

Each cookbook author has their own ways of writing a recipe. Here are the abbreviations that you will find in this book:

Recipe Abbreviations
t. = teaspoon(s)
T. = Tablespoon(s)
c. = cup(s)
oz. = ounce(s)
qt. = quart(s)
pkg. = package
lb. = pound(s)

Ingredient Substitutions

It is important to know some key substitutions for foods that commonly cause IC and OAB problems. You may have to experiment to find out which substitutions work best, while not substantially changing the quality of the recipe:

In place of:	Try:
Tomatoes	Red bell pepper for color, flavor, and nutrition. Substitute pesto or white sauces on pasta.
Lemon juice for flavor	Zest (grated peel) of lemon or lemon oil flavoring
Lemon juice or vinegar	Pear juice or blueberry juice
Chocolate	White chocolate, butterscotch, caramel, or vanilla products
Canned soups	Fresh soups made with safe ingredients
Strawberries	Blueberries (raspberries, blackberries, or rhubarb as tolerated)
Apples	Pears (For baked goods that require firmer fruit, choose pears that are not quite ripe.)
Prepared salad dressings	Yogurt, blended cottage cheese, or buttermilk (if tolerated) as a base for creamy dressings–add seasoning. Make your own homemade "vinegar" and oil by substituting pear juice or blueberry juice for the vinegar. Or, simply use flavor-infused olive oils.
Hard cheeses like cheddar	Softer cheeses like cottage cheese, ricotta, feta, cream cheese, provolone, or mozzarella
Peanuts, pecans, walnuts, macadamia nuts	Almonds, cashews, pine nuts
Bouillon (chicken or beef)	MSG-free, organic broth and/or bouillon
Sausages	Ground beef, pork, chicken or turkey seasoned with safe herbs and spices

Breakfast

Breakfast

While there are some breakfast foods that can increase bladder symptoms, most items on the breakfast menu are actually soothing to a fussy bladder. If you are flaring, a simple meal of eggs and toast can even make a good dinner.

What should you watch out for? Sausages and other breakfast-type meats usually have high levels of nitrates and other preservatives. You may find some organic sausages or bacons will work better for you. Also, some cereals are highly fortified with vitamins. Since interstitial cystitis patients are usually sensitive to "mega" doses of vitamins, you should avoid cereals that claim to have 100% of any nutrient, especially vitamin C and the B vitamins. Of course, many juices and fruits seem to cause an increase in bladder symptoms, but pears and blueberries are usually okay, and many patients find that they can occasionally eat small amounts of other fruits like bananas, sweet apples, and even low-acid orange juice.

Although I won't go into too many different ways to prepare your eggs, I will give you some helpful hints to make things a little easier in the morning. For example, did you know you can make scrambled eggs in the microwave?

One-Minute Microwave Scrambled Eggs

Spray the inside of a microwave-safe bowl or a 1 c. glass measuring cup with a cooking spray like Pam® or Wesson®. Crack two eggs into the bowl; add 1/2 t. milk, and whisk with a fork until fluffy. Heat in a microwave on medium heat for 20 seconds. Remove eggs, stir with the fork. Heat in microwave again for another 20 seconds. Fluff up again with the fork. Return to microwave one last time on medium heat for 10 seconds. Eggs should be mostly firm with a slight amount of moisture. Let rest for 5 to 10 seconds to finish cooking and enjoy!

Spinach and Feta Quiche

Julie's Favorites: This was a hit last year on Christmas morning!

Ingredients

- 2 (10 oz.) pkg. frozen chopped spinach (thawed)
- 3 eggs
- 1 c. half and half (may substitute 1 c. evaporated skim milk)
- 1 c. crumbled feta cheese (4 oz.)
- 2 T. chopped green onions
- 1/2 t. lemon zest, if tolerated
- 1/2 t. salt
- 1/4 t. pepper
- 1 unbaked 9-inch pie shell (may use refrigerator or frozen dough)

Pierce bottom of pie shell and bake for 5 minutes at 350°F. Cool slightly. Raise temperature of oven to 400°F.

Drain spinach and press out all liquid. (This can be done easily between layers of paper towels.) Set aside.

Whisk eggs and half-and-half or milk in bowl. Add cheese, green onions, lemon zest, salt, and pepper. Pour into partially baked pie shell. Bake on middle rack, 400°F for 10 minutes, reducing oven temperature to 350°F for the last 25 minutes.

Broccoli and Mozzarella Quiche: Substitute 1 cup frozen broccoli florets for the spinach and 1/2 cup mozzarella cheese for the feta cheese.

Blueberry Breakfast Casserole

Ingredients

- 12 slices homemade-type white bread
- 16 oz. cream cheese, cubed
- 1 c. fresh blueberries
- 12 large eggs
- 1/3 c. maple syrup
- 2 c. milk

Sauce Ingredients

- 1 c. sugar
- 2 T. cornstarch
- 1 c. water
- 1 c. fresh blueberries
- 1 T. unsalted butter

Prepare the night before: Remove crusts from bread and cube bread into 1-inch pieces. Layer ingredients in a buttered 9 x 13-inch glass baking dish:

1. Half of the bread cubes (the bottom)
2. Cubed cream cheese
3. Blueberries
4. Other half of the bread cubes

In large bowl, whisk together eggs, syrup, and milk. Pour over bread/blueberry layers. Cover, and chill overnight.

In the morning: Preheat oven to 350°F. Cover casserole with foil and bake for 30 minutes or until puffy and golden brown.

For blueberry sauce: Stir sugar, cornstarch, and water in small saucepan. Cook mixture over medium heat for 5 minutes, stirring frequently. Mixture will thicken. Stir in blueberries and simmer the mixture, stirring frequently, about 10 minutes or until berries have "burst." Add butter and stir the sauce until butter is melted. Serve casserole with sauce.

Blueberry Pancakes
From www.mealsforyou.com

Ingredients
- 1 c. all purpose flour
- 1/2 t. baking soda
- 3/4 t. baking powder
- 2 T. sugar
- 1/2 t. salt
- 1 c. buttermilk
- 2 T. vegetable oil
- 1 egg, lightly beaten
- 1 c. blueberries, thawed and drained, if frozen

Sift flour, baking soda, baking powder, sugar, and salt together in a large bowl. Combine buttermilk, oil, and egg in another bowl. Stir buttermilk mixture into dry ingredients until just combined. Do not over mix. Heat a heavy nonstick skillet or griddle over medium high heat to 375°F. When hot, lightly brush surface with oil. Add about 1/3 c. of batter per pancake to skillet. Sprinkle a few blueberries over each round of pancake batter and cook 2-3 minutes, or until small holes appear in batter and bottom is browned. Turn cakes and cook about 1 minute or until browned. Repeat process until all pancakes are cooked. Serve immediately with desired toppings or keep warm in a 200°F oven until ready to serve.

Flax Seed Pancakes: Add 4 T. ground flax seed to the batter instead of the blueberries for a wonderful nutty flavor. Flax seed is rich in omega-3 fatty acids. Buy flax seed whole and grind in a coffee grinder or buy it already ground in a vacuum sealed package. Store unused ground flax seed in the freezer to prolong the product's freshness.

Maple Blueberry Waffles

Ingredients
- 2 T. maple syrup
- 4 beaten egg yolks (save egg whites to add in next step)
- 1-1/2 c. milk
- 1 c. plain organic yogurt (if not tolerated, increase milk to 2 c.)
- 7 T. melted butter
- 2 c. whole wheat or unbleached white pastry flour
- 2-1/2 t. baking powder
- 3/4 t. baking soda
- 1/2 t. salt
- 4 beaten egg whites (stiff)
- 1 pint blueberries (smaller Maine berries work best)

Combine maple syrup, egg yolks, milk, yogurt, and butter. In a separate bowl, sift together dry ingredients. Slowly add dry mixture to wet, stirring gently as you go. Blend just until everything is combined. Do not over-stir mixture.

Fold in stiffly beaten egg whites and blueberries. Cook waffles according to your waffle iron or maker's instructions. Serve with maple syrup or fresh blueberries. Makes 10 8-inch waffles.

Basic French Toast

Ingredients
- 3 large eggs
- 1/2 c. milk plus 1/2 t. vanilla
- 8 to 10 slices bread (try different grains or even **cinnamon** bread)

Crack eggs into a pie plate or other wide, but shallow pan; beat lightly with a fork. Stir in milk and vanilla. Melt enough butter in griddle or skillet to coat the bottom.

Dip the bread slices into the egg mixture, wetting one side, then the other. Hint: Do not over "soak" bread and only dip what you can make in one batch.

Place bread slices on hot griddle or skillet, heating slowly until bottom is golden brown. Turn with pancake turner or spatula and brown the other side. Serve with hot syrup, sprinkle with powdered sugar, or spread with Low-Acid Blueberry "Jam."

Low-Acid Blueberry "Jam"

From: *A Taste of the Good Life: A Cookbook for an Interstitial Cystitis Diet* by Beverley Laumann

The recipe below makes a delicious spread for toast. Not a true jam, it must be kept in the refrigerator.

Ingredients
- 1/2 c. sugar
- 2 T. flour
- 1 t. Knox unflavored gelatin
- 1/4 t. ground cinnamon
- 2 c. fresh, ripe blueberries
- 1/4 t. lemon extract (optional)
- 6 T. water

Thoroughly mix the sugar, flour, gelatin, and cinnamon in a saucepan. Add blueberries, lemon extract, and water. Heat while stirring, coating the blueberries with the sugar. Bring to a boil over medium to high heat, stirring continuously to prevent scorching. Continue stirring and cooking one minute more. Pour into a heat-resistant container to cool. Store covered in the refrigerator until ready to use

Good for You Granola

Printed with permission Quaker Oats Company

Ingredients

- 3–1/2 c. Quaker Oats®, old fashioned, uncooked
- 1/2 c. sliced unblanched almonds (if tolerated)
- 1/3 c. honey
- 1/4 c. vegetable oil
- 1 t. ground cinnamon
- 1 t. vanilla
- 1/4 t. ground nutmeg

Heat oven to 350°F. In large bowl combine oats and almonds. In small bowl stir together honey, oil, cinnamon, vanilla, and nutmeg. Drizzle over oat mixture; mix well. Spread evenly in 13 x 9 x 2-inch baking pan.

Bake 15 to 20 minutes or until golden brown, stirring every 5 minutes. Remove from oven; cool completely in pan on wire rack. Store tightly covered for up to 2 weeks.

Fancy Oatmeal

Are you are a bladder patient who cannot use the pre-packaged, instant oatmeal that is popular today? Then it is time to start experimenting on your own. You can either make the oatmeal by the package directions (I like using the old fashioned kind where I can actually see the oatmeal flakes), or you can put 1/2 c. uncooked oatmeal in a bowl, add 1/2 c. water, and microwave for one minute. Then, try these add-ins:

- Diced canned pears (with juice)
- Brown sugar and cinnamon
- Ground flax seed
- Chopped almonds
- Dried or fresh blueberries
- Blueberry jam
- Vanilla yogurt or cottage cheese

"It's up to You" Omelet

Ingredients
- 3 eggs
- 2 T. milk
- 1/2 T. flour or pancake mix
- Pinch salt, pepper, if tolerated, to taste
- Butter or cooking spray
- Non-stick omelet pan (or 8" frying pan with sloped sides)

Whisk eggs, milk, and flour together until frothy. (You can also use a blender for 10 to 15 seconds on medium high). Using medium high heat, melt enough butter to cover all surfaces of the pan or use a light coat of cooking spray.

When pan is hot, pour in egg mixture and let cook. Use a rubber spatula to poke any large bubbles that form. When edges begin to pull away from the sides of the pan, carefully flip omelet over. Add your choice of ingredients from list below. Cook for 60 seconds or so. Turn out on plate, flipping one half over the other.

Variations:
- Shredded cooked chicken
- Ground beef
- Cream cheese (cubed or sliced thinly)
- Mozzarella or provolone cheese
- Feta cheese
- Fresh spinach
- Fresh or frozen broccoli
- Green, red, orange, and/or yellow bell pepper
- Shredded carrot
- Chopped onion or green onion
- Chives
- Mushrooms, sliced
- Corn and black beans

Appetizers & Snacks

Appetizers & Snacks

You don't have to avoid parties or other social gatherings simply because you are afraid there won't be anything for you to eat. Naturally, if you are giving a party, you have control over the menu. Start with simple foods like sliced meats, vegetable trays, and all-natural snacks like potato chips, pretzels, and pita chips. You can also make minor changes to some party staples, like vegetable dips and desserts. If you are invited to a party, you can always call the host to find out what is on the menu. You don't have to apologize for this. In fact there is a sneaky way to find out the menu without being obvious. Ask if you can bring something from the menu. Naturally, you would want to pick at least one thing you can eat.

You also can eat a small meal before you go to fill yourself up. That way you will have more willpower to choose bladder-friendly foods; and if there isn't much, you won't be starving. So, get ready to party! Here are some recipes for appetizers and snacks that are fun and safe to eat.

Deviled Eggs

Ingredients
- 6 fresh eggs
- 2 T. Basil Buttermilk Salad Dressing (pg. 56)

Put eggs in large pot and cover with cool water. Eggs should be able to lie on the bottom of the pot without touching. Bring the water to a rapid boil. Cover pot and remove from heat, keeping the eggs in the hot water for 10 to 12 minutes. (Cooking and resting time may need to be adjusted depending on the type of pan you use.)

Using large slotted spoon, take eggs out of hot water and put in a large dish of ice water. This will stop the cooking process. Let rest for 5 to 10 minutes. Peel eggs under cool running tap water.

Cut eggs in half and remove yolks to separate bowl. Crumble yolks with fork and mix in dressing. Put heaping teaspoonful of mixture back into each half egg. Makes 12.

Homemade Tortilla Chips

Ingredients
- 12 8-inch flour or corn tortillas
- Butter flavor cooking spray
- 1 t. finely ground salt

Preheat oven to 350°F. Cut each tortilla into 8 to 10 pie-shaped wedges. (You can also cut into strips if preferred.) Place on an ungreased baking sheet in a single layer. Spray chips lightly with cooking spray; sprinkle salt on chips. Bake 10 to 15 minutes, watching closely to prevent burning.

Variations:

Herbed Tortilla Chips: Add 1/4 t. each basil, thyme, and rosemary, and a dash of garlic to salt before sprinkling on chips.

"Kettle" Tortilla Chips: Substitute mixture of 1 t. extra fine granulated sugar and 1/2 t. finely ground salt for the 1 t. salt.

Sweet Tortilla Chips: Substitute 2 t. extra fine granulated sugar, or cinnamon sugar mix (2 t. extra fine sugar mixed with 1/4 t. ground cinnamon) for the 1 t. salt.

Homemade Spinach Dip

Ingredients

- 10 oz. box frozen chopped spinach (thaw, drain, and press out excess liquid)
- 1 c. fat-free plain yogurt (try organic Greek yogurt!)
- 1/2 c. low-fat cottage cheese
- 1/2 t. lemon or orange zest
- 1 t. dill
- 2 t. parsley
- 1 t. minced garlic
- 1/4 c. chopped green onions (if tolerated)
- 2 t. finely chopped red pepper
- Pinch onion powder
- Salt and pepper to taste (if tolerated)
- 1 small can water chestnuts, drained and coarsely chopped

Begin 1 to 2 hours ahead of time. Thaw spinach. Place mesh strainer over medium bowl; insert coffee filter into strainer. Measure yogurt and cottage cheese into coffee filter and refrigerate for one to two hours while allowing liquid to drain into bowl.

After yogurt and cottage cheese have drained, blend all ingredients EXCEPT spinach and water chestnuts in blender or food processor until smooth.

Fold in spinach and chopped water chestnuts. Serve chilled. Store in refrigerator for up to one week past "sell-by" dates on yogurt and cottage cheese.

Amy's Microwave Caramel Corn

Ingredients
- 1 c. brown sugar
- 1/2 c. butter
- 1/4 c. white corn syrup
- 1/2 t. salt
- 1/2 t. baking soda
- 3 qt. popped corn
- 2 large grocery bags (put one inside the other)

Combine brown sugar, butter, syrup, and salt in a 4-cup microwave-safe container. Cook for 2 minutes on high. After mixture comes to a rolling boil, add baking soda and stir well.

Place popcorn in doubled bag and pour the sugar/butter mixture over it. Fold the edge of the bag to close and return to the microwave. Cook on high for 1-1/2 minutes. Remove and shake well. Return to the microwave for another 1/2 minute. Remove, shake, and eat!

Kettle Corn

Ingredients
- 1/2 c. un-popped popcorn
- 1/4 c. cooking oil
- 1/2 c. granulated sugar
- 1/4 t. salt

Place the popcorn, cooking oil, and sugar in a large pot, covering with a tight lid. Cook over medium heat, shaking constantly to make sure the popcorn doesn't burn. Once the popping has slowed, remove the pot from heat. Shake salt over kettle corn, and enjoy!

Carrot Pinwheels

Ingredients
- 1/4 c. softened cream cheese
- 1/4 c. Homemade and Healthy Ranch Dip (pg. 57)
- 4 8-in. flour tortillas
- 2 c. finely shredded carrots
- 2 green onions, chopped (if tolerated)

Blend together cream cheese and dip. Warm each tortilla in microwave for 5 seconds to soften. Spread cream cheese mixture on tortilla. Sprinkle carrots and onion over mixture. Roll each tortilla tightly; wrap in plastic wrap. Repeat for each tortilla. Refrigerate at least 30 minutes.

Unwrap when ready to serve. Cut each tortilla roll into six pieces with a sharp, serrated knife.

Honey Pear Pinwheels

Ingredients
- 1 T. honey
- 1/4 c. softened cream cheese
- 1/4 c. cottage cheese (liquid drained off)
- 1-1/2 c. shredded ripe pear (about 2 pears)
- 1/2 t. cinnamon, if desired
- 4 8-in. flour tortillas

Put honey, cream cheese, and cottage cheese in blender and blend until creamy. Toss cinnamon into shredded pears, if desired. Sprinkle pears over mixture. Roll each tortilla tightly; wrap in plastic wrap. Repeat for each tortilla.
Refrigerate at least 30 minutes.

Unwrap when ready to serve. Cut each tortilla roll into six pieces with a sharp, serrated knife.

Slow Cooker Swedish Meatballs

Ingredients
- 1-1/2 c. fresh bread crumbs
- 1 c. milk or cream
- 1-1/2 lbs. ground chuck
- 1/2 lb. lean ground pork
- 2 eggs
- 1 medium onion, chopped fine
- 1-3/4 t. salt
- 1/4 t. allspice
- 1/8 t. nutmeg
- 1/8 t. pepper
- 2 c. beef stock (pg. 52) or 1 16-oz. can organic beef broth
- 2 T. butter, melted
- 2 T. flour

Soak bread crumbs in milk for 5 minutes in a large mixing bowl. Add beef, pork, eggs, onion, 1-1/2 tsp. salt, allspice, and nutmeg. Mix well. Shape into 1-inch balls. Place on broiler pan and bake for 15 minutes at 400°F.

Put browned meatballs in slow cooker. Add 1/2 beef stock, pepper and remaining salt. Cover and cook on low 4-6 hours (high 2-3 hours).

To thicken gravy, turn slow cooker to high. Combine butter and flour to make a smooth paste. Add paste to remaining beef stock and pour into crock pot. Cook until thickened, about 45 minutes.

Veggie Pizza

Ingredients
- 1 pizza crust (pg. 61)
- 1/2 t. olive oil
- 8 oz. cream cheese, softened
- 2 T. Basil Buttermilk Salad Dressing (pg. 56) or Homemade and Healthy Ranch Dressing (pg. 57)
- Salt and pepper to taste
- 2 T. fresh basil, coarsely chopped
- 2 c. chopped vegetables [can use zucchini, green onions, bell peppers (red, yellow, orange, or green), mushrooms, cucumbers, carrots, broccoli, or other vegetables as tolerated.]
- 1/2 c. crumbled feta cheese

Bake pizza crust at 350°F for 10 to 12 minutes or until lightly browned. Cool at least 30 minutes. Mix together olive oil, cream cheese, and salad dressing. Spread mixture over pizza crust. Sprinkle basil and vegetables on top. Evenly distribute feta cheese over vegetables. Serve chilled.

Crab Stuffed Mushrooms

Ingredients
- 1 T. butter
- 1 T. minced garlic
- 30-35 large fresh mushrooms, stems removed
- 2 c. crab meat, cooked
- 4 oz. cream cheese
- 2 T. green onions, finely chopped
- Salt, pepper to taste

Melt the butter in a skillet and add the garlic. Briefly fry the mushroom caps until lightly browned. Remove from pan and allow to cool. Combine the crab meat, cream cheese, and green onion. Add salt and pepper to taste. Mix well. Stuff mushroom caps with a spoonful of the crab mixture each. Bake at 350°F for 10-15 minutes or until lightly browned.

Crab Dip

Ingredients
- 1 8-oz. pkg. cream cheese, softened
- 1 T. milk
- 1 c. Maryland lump crabmeat (may use canned)
- 2 T chopped green onion
- 1/4 t. minced garlic
- salt and pepper to taste, if tolerates
- 2 oz. pkg. chopped almonds

Combine cream cheese, milk, crabmeat (drain if from canned), onion, and garlic in medium mixing bowl. Add salt and pepper. Spread in 8 x 8 inch shallow baking dish; sprinkle almonds on top. Bake at 350°F for 20 minutes. Surface should be lightly browned. Serve hot with crackers.

Soups

Soups

Many people with bladder problems cannot use canned soups because they contain tomato products, monosodium glutamate (MSG), vinegar, or even mystery ingredients listed on the labels as "natural and artificial flavorings."

The good news is that homemade soups are easy to make, and the recipes are easily modified. If you cannot use onion or pepper, leave them out. If you like one vegetable more than another, leave one out and add more of what you like. For those who cannot use canned chicken or beef broth (even if it is organic and MSG-free), you can save pan drippings from roasted meats to add flavor, or make your own stock from leftovers. The world of soups is endless and can be a great source of comfort foods for those iffy days.

Cream Soup Substitute

A great way to begin! Use this soup substitute as a base for many of your favorite dishes that require canned cream of mushroom, cream of celery, or cream of chicken soup.

Ingredients:
- 2 T. butter or margarine
- 2 T. flour
- 12 oz. can of skim evaporated milk
- 1/2 t. salt
- 1/4. t. garlic powder
- 1 T. onion chopped fine (or use chopped chives if you are sensitive to onion)
- 1/4 t. pepper, if tolerated.

Melt butter in medium saucepan over medium heat. Add flour blending with whisk until smooth. Slowly add milk, whisking constantly until mixture thickens, remove from heat. Blend in seasonings.

To use instead of canned cream soups in recipes:

- **Simple soup**: Add mushrooms, celery or chicken, 1 c. skim milk, cooked vegetables.
- **Casserole**: Add 1 c. chopped chicken or tuna, vegetables and 3 c. noodles. Bake at 350°F for 20 minutes
- **Hearty Soup**: Add 1 c. chicken, 1 1/2 c. skim milk, 2 cubed potatoes, 2 diced carrots, 1/2 c. peas, and 1 stalk chopped celery. Simmer over medium heat until vegetables are cooked through.
- **Broccoli Soup**: Add 1 c. cooked broccoli, put in blender and give it a whirl!
- **Quick White Pizza**: Put 2-3 T. of sauce on a pita. Add strips of baked or grilled chicken, mushrooms, sprinkle with basil, top with mozzarella cheese and bake until bubbly.

Creating Your Own Soup Base (Stock)

What did people do before they had canned broth products? They made their own soup bases from leftover bones and vegetables. Homemade soup bases take some time to make, but the process is fairly easy, and you can freeze soup bases for months. If you choose a cold winter day to make your stock, you have the added benefit of filling your kitchen with a little heat and humidity—not to mention that yummy aroma!

You can search for various techniques on the internet, but here is a basic recipe to get you started:

Ingredients

- 3 to 4 cups bones, skin, trimmings of chicken, turkey or beef cuts. (If you don't cook large meals often, consider keeping a container in your freezer where you can put small amounts of scraps to save up until you are ready to use. You can also freeze your turkey carcass after a Thanksgiving meal to make stock with at a later date.)
- 1 large onion, quartered
- 3 to 4 stalks celery with leaves, cut in 2-inch sections
- 5 to 6 carrots cut into 2-inch sections
- 1/2 c. parsley, chopped
- 1/2 c. other chopped fresh herbs (basil, rosemary, marjoram, thyme)
- 1/2 t. salt
- 1/2 t. pepper, if tolerated

Add ingredients to large stock pot and cover with water. Bring to a boil and simmer on low for 4 or more hours. (You can also put ingredients in a large crock pot to simmer, but boil the water first, before you put it over the other ingredients.) The longer you simmer, the more concentrated the flavor will be.

Line a colander with two layers of cheesecloth. Remove bones and other large pieces from the stock; then strain remaining product through the colander and cheesecloth. Divide resultant soup base/stock into 1 cup portions and freeze for up to 6 months. Use in many recipes, including those that follow!

Rosemary Chicken Noodle Soup

Ingredients
- 1 T. olive oil
- 2 c. water
- 1 can MSG-free chicken broth or 2 c. homemade chicken soup base
- 1 c. cubed chicken
- 1 celery stalk, cut into bite size pieces
- 2 carrots, peeled and cut into bite size "coins"
- 1/2 c. frozen peas
- 1/4 c. chopped onion, if tolerated
- 2 T. finely chopped fresh rosemary
- Salt and pepper to taste, if tolerated
- 2 oz. thin egg noodles

Combine all ingredients except egg noodles on stove in large sauce pan then heat to a boil. Simmer soup until vegetables are slightly cooked (al dente). Add egg noodles and continue to cook for 5 to 10 minutes until noodles are cooked through. Serves 6.

Julie's Potato Soup

Ingredients Pot #1
- 2 c. water
- 10 oz. can chicken broth, MSG-free
- 1 t. salt
- 1/8 t. ground pepper
- 2 T. fresh chopped basil
- 2 T. fresh chopped parsley
- 1 T. minced garlic
- 1 medium onion – chopped into 1/4-inch pieces
- 3 carrots, peeled and sliced into "coins"
- 2 stalks celery, cut into 1/4-inch pieces
- 1/3 c. red bell pepper, cut into 1/4-inch pieces.
- 3 medium potatoes, cubed

Combine all ingredients in 4 qt. pot. Heat on stove, medium-high. When mixture reaches a boil, reduce temperature to maintain a simmer while preparing other ingredients:

Ingredients Pot #2
- 2 T. butter
- 2 T. flour
- 1 1/2 c. skim or low-fat milk (may substitute one 12- oz. can evaporated skim milk)
- 8 oz. cream cheese

Hold until last:
- 10 oz. bag frozen "baby broccoli" florets (**Do not thaw**)

Melt butter over low to medium heat in 1 qt. saucepan. Whisk in flour being careful not to burn mixture. Slowly add milk, continuing to whisk until entire mixture has thickened. Add cream cheese one tablespoon at a time as you continue to whisk.

When vegetables in larger pot are cooked (about 10 to 12 minutes), turn off heat and add **frozen** broccoli to mixture.

Note: This step allows the broccoli to cook slightly while lowering the temperature of the mixture so that you can safely add the milk/cheese mixture.

When broccoli has been heated thoroughly, slowly add milk/cheese mixture to the larger pot, stirring continually. Bring temperature back up slowly. Do not overheat. Serves 6 to 8. Freezes and reheats well.

Savory Salmon Soup

Ingredients
- 3 T. butter
- 3 T. flour
- 3 c. whole milk (may substitute two 12-ounce cans evaporated skim milk)
- 4 to 5 oz. can salmon (no skin or bones—drained)
- 3 T. chopped fresh thyme (may substitute rosemary or basil for different flavor)
- Salt and pepper to taste

Melt butter over low to medium heat in 2 qt. saucepan. Whisk in flour being careful not to burn mixture. Slowly add milk, continuing to whisk until entire mixture has thickened. Add salmon, thyme, salt and pepper. Heat through; serve warm with dollop of plain yogurt if desired.

Butternut Squash Soup

Recipe adapted from Alicia's Recipes: www.aliciasrecipes.com

Ingredients

- 2 T. unsalted butter
- 1 small onion
- 1 T. fresh rosemary (1 tsp. dried)
- 1 small butternut squash (chopped)
- 6 1/3 c. chicken stock (50.4 oz.)
- 1 1/4-cup heavy cream (may substitute 12 oz. evaporated skim milk)
- 1 t. salt
- 1/2 t. white pepper, if tolerated

Melt butter over moderate heat in large saucepan. Add the onion and rosemary and cook until soft (approx. 5 min.) Add chopped squash, chicken stock, heavy cream, salt, and white pepper. Reduce heat and cover. Simmer for approx. 2 hours - or until squash is tender. Use blender to puree the hot soup.

Nutrition Note: Did you know that one cup of butternut squash, cubed, has only 80 calories, provides over 400% of your daily requirement for vitamin A, and over half of your vitamin C requirements for the day!

Slow Cooker Vegetable Beef Soup

Ingredients
- 2 c. leftover roast beef or 2 lbs. fresh round steak, trimmed and cubed
- 3 c. water
- 1 16-oz. can organic beef broth (no MSG) or 2. c. homemade beef stock
- 2 large potatoes, peeled and cubed
- 3 carrots, peeled and sliced
- 2 stalks celery, sliced
- 1 T. dried basil
- 1 to 2 t. salt
- 1/4 t. pepper, if tolerated
- 1/2 c. peas (thaw if frozen)
- 1/2 c. corn (thaw if frozen)
- 1/2 c. green beans (thaw if frozen)
- 1/2 c. kidney or red beans (from canned, drain off liquid)

If using fresh round steak: Heat 1 T. olive or canola oil in skillet, and lightly brown steak cubes.

Microwave or heat water and broth until boiling. (Heating liquids first helps bring soup to a safe temperature more quickly.) Add hot liquid and other ingredients to 3 qt. or larger slow cooker. Cook on low 6 to 8 hours, or on high 4 to 6 hours until meat is tender and vegetables are cooked through. Serves 6.

Vanilla Pumpkin Soup

Published with permission of www.VanillaShop.com

Ingredients

- 1 pumpkin
- 2 onions
- 1 leek
- 1 T. butter
- 16 oz. chicken broth, canned or homemade
- 3 c. water
- 1/4 c. heavy cream
- 1/2 c. milk
- 1 vanilla bean or 1 t. pure ground vanilla
- Salt and pepper to taste

Cut pumpkin in cubes; slice onions and leek. Combine vegetables, chicken bouillon or base, and water in a soup pot, cover. Bring to a boil, reduce heat and simmer for 45 minutes until vegetables are tender.

Meanwhile, bring milk to a boil in microwave. Remove and add vanilla bean split lengthwise or pure ground vanilla. Let infuse for 20 minutes.

Blend the mixtures in a blender or food processor. Return to pot and warm over low heat. Add butter, cream and vanilla-infused milk. Season with salt and pepper, if desired. Serve in soup plates and garnish with fresh basil leaves. Makes 4 servings.

Chicken Corn Chowder

Ingredients
- 2 T. butter
- 2 T. flour
- 4 c. skim or low-fat milk (may substitute two, 12 ounce cans evaporated skim milk)
- 1 cup cubed, cooked chicken
- 1 can (15 to 16 oz.) bi-color corn
- 1/4 c. finely chopped red bell pepper (if desired)
- 1 large potato, peeled and cubed
- 1 t. salt
- 1/4 t. pepper, if tolerated.

Melt butter over low to medium heat in 1 qt sauce pan. Whisk in flour being careful not to burn mixture. Slowly add milk, continuing to whisk until entire mixture thickens.

While still heating, add chicken, can of corn (including liquid), pepper, cubed potato, salt and pepper. While continuously stirring, bring mixture to a simmer. Continue to stir and simmer mixture 10 to 12 minutes, or until potatoes are cooked.

Salads, Salad Dressings, & Spreads

Salads, Salad Dressings, and Spreads

One of the most common questions I get from interstitial cystitis (IC) patients is, *"What can I put on my salad?"* My answer is, *"Plenty!"* The trick is to pile the salad itself with flavorful vegetables, herbs, fruit, cheeses, and nuts so that you aren't relying solely on the salad dressing for that burst of flavor. You can also try herb-infused oils for salad dressing (available from the Interstitial Cystitis Network Shop: www.icnsales.com) or create homemade dressings with suitable substitutes for the vinegar or mayonnaise base. You can even make your own croutons (pg. 65). Finally, as always, rely on your own instincts and experience with various ingredients. Enjoy!

Carrot Salad with Honey Dressing
From: *A Taste of the Good Life: A Cookbook for an Interstitial Cystitis Diet* by Beverley Laumann

Ingredients:
- 2 c. grated carrot
- 2 t. fresh mint, finely chopped
- 4 t. dried parsley
- 2 T. raisins (optional)
- 2 t. canola oil
- 1/2 t. ground coriander
- 2 t. honey
- Dash salt

Mix grated carrot, mint, parsley, and raisins, if desired, in a salad bowl. Combine oil, coriander, honey, and salt, whisking together until blended. Pour over salad, tossing to blend. Chill and serve.

Sautéed Pear Salad

Adapted with permission of The Vanilla.COMpany (www.vanilla.com)

Ingredients

- 1 T. olive oil
- 2 firm-ripe pears, cored, peeled and cut into slices
- 1 T. honey
- 8 c. salad greens and/or baby spinach leaves, rinsed and chilled
- 1/2 c. each thinly sliced cucumber, carrots, and red bell peppers
- 4 oz. feta or goat cheese
- 1 c. chopped roasted or glazed almond pieces (if tolerated)
- 1/3 c. olive oil
- 3 T. pear juice
- 1 T. honey
- 1 t. pure vanilla extract
- Salt and pepper to taste

Heat large frying pan over medium-high heat. Add olive oil and allow to warm. Add pear slices and sauté in oil for 2 minutes on each side. Turn off heat and drizzle honey over pear slices; gently turn pears so that honey coats them on both sides.

While pears are cooking, put greens and vegetables into a large salad bowl and mix well. Add warm pears, cheese, nuts and gently mix.

Mix salad dressing ingredients, add juices from pan and pour over salad. Serve immediately.

Note: You can also add grilled chicken slices or prawns to this salad and serve with crusty bread as a main course.

Pear and Honey Coleslaw

Ingredients:
- 1 hard (not ripe) pear
- 2 c. shredded white and red cabbage
- 1/2 c. shredded carrots
- 1/2 t. finely chopped mint, if desired
- 1/2 c. pear juice
- 1/4 c. canola oil
- 1 t. lemon zest
- 1 T. honey
- 1/2 t. sea salt
- 1/4 t. pepper

Peel, core, and grate pear to equal 1/2 cup. Combine with cabbage and carrots. Place mint, pear juice, canola oil, lemon zest, honey, salt, and pepper in blender and mix until well blended. Pour immediately over vegetables and toss. Refrigerate a minimum of 4 hours, stirring occasionally to blend flavors. May also be served as a hot salad by microwaving for 30 seconds per serving.

Avocado Spread for Sandwiches

Ingredients
- 1 seeded and peeled avocado
- 1 to 2 t. finely chopped chives
- 1 T. pear juice
- 1 T. finely chopped fresh dill
- Salt and pepper as tolerated to taste

Mash avocado with a fork. Gently combine other ingredients. Spread on bread and add your choice of cooked meat (leftover chicken, turkey, and pork work well).

To Use as a Dip for Vegetables, Crackers, or Chips: Increase pear juice to 3 T. and use 2 T. finely chopped cilantro in place of dill (if tolerated).

Red, White and Blue Spinach Salad

Ingredients
- 1 c. washed baby spinach leaves
- 1 c. washed baby red bib lettuce, torn to bite size pieces
- 1/2 c. fresh blueberries, washed and drained
- 1/2 c. slivered almonds
- 1/2 c. feta cheese (if desired)
- 2 T. coarsely chopped fresh basil (if desired)

Combine spinach and red lettuce in large salad bowl. Sprinkle blueberries, almonds, and cheese over lettuce. (Hint: Even if you can't have tomatoes, others you are serving the salad to may want them. Add a handful of tiny grape tomatoes to the salad that will be easy for you to push aside or avoid.)

Drizzle with Basil Blueberry Non-Vinaigrette Salad Dressing:

Basil Blueberry Non-Vinaigrette Salad Dressing

Ingredients
- 1 c. frozen blueberries, partially thawed
- 1/2 c. organic, pure blueberry juice
- 1/2 c. olive oil
- 1 t. lemon zest
- 1/2 t. sugar
- 2 t. finely chopped fresh basil (may substitute thyme)
- Pinch salt
- Pinch white pepper as tolerated to taste

Place all ingredients in blender. Blend using one-second "pulses," checking consistency after every couple of pulses.

May also be made without using frozen berries. Simply increase juice to 1 cup.

Fresh Garden Salad

Ingredients
- 1 c. washed and torn leaf lettuce
- 1 c. romaine lettuce
- 1/2 c. shredded red cabbage
- 1/2 c. shredded carrots
- 1/2 c. chopped green onion, if tolerated
- 1 t. coarsely chopped fresh basil (if desired)
- 1 t. coarsely chopped fresh thyme (if desired)
- 1 t. coarsely chopped parsley (if desired)
- 1/2 red bell pepper, seeded and cut in thin strips
- 1/2 c. mushrooms, cleaned and sliced thinly
- 1/2 c. homemade whole grain croutons
- 1 cucumber, sliced for garnish

Toss together lettuces, cabbage, carrots, and herbs in a large salad bowl. Arrange red bell pepper strips, mushrooms, croutons, and cucumbers on top.

Serve with Buttermilk Basil Salad Dressing. Top with hard boiled egg slices and cooked chicken breast strips for a main dish salad!

Buttermilk Basil Salad Dressing

Ingredients
- 2 c. fresh basil, chopped finely
- 2 green onions
- 3/4 c. buttermilk
- 3/4 c. low-fat cottage cheese
- 1 t. lemon zest
- 1/2 t. salt
- 1/2 t. pepper

Combine fresh basil, green onions, buttermilk, and cottage cheese in blender. Blend until smooth. Add lemon zest, salt, and pepper and whisk together.

For sandwich spread: Reduce buttermilk to 1/2 c. and drain liquid from cottage cheese before blending.

Homemade and Healthy Ranch Dip & Dressing

Ingredients
- 1 c. fat-free plain yogurt (try organic Greek yogurt!)
- 1/2 c. low-fat cottage cheese
- 1/2 t. lemon zest
- 1 t. dill
- 2 t. parsley
- 1/4 t. minced garlic
- Pinch onion powder
- Pinch sugar
- Salt and pepper to taste, if tolerated

Blend all ingredients in blender or food processor until smooth. Store in refrigerator for up to one week past "sell-by" dates on yogurt and cottage cheese.

For sandwich spread: Begin 1 to 2 hours ahead of time. Place mesh strainer over medium bowl; insert coffee filter into strainer. Measure yogurt and cottage cheese into coffee filter and refrigerate for one to two hours while allowing liquid to drain into bowl. After yogurt and cottage cheese have drained, blend all ingredients in blender or food processor until smooth. If spread is too thick, add strained liquid back 1/2 t. at a time until spreadable.

Breads &
Baked Goods

Breads & Baked Goods

Generally, people with interstitial cystitis or overactive bladder do not have problems tolerating bread and baked goods. If you do seem to react to the preservatives in store-bought baked goods, you can make almost everything from scratch at home. Here are some examples; hopefully you will find a few new things to add to your menus.

Amish White Bread

Ingredients
- 2 c. warm water (110°F)
- 2/3 c. white sugar
- 1-1/2 T. active dry yeast
- 1-1/2 t. salt
- 1/4 c. vegetable oil
- 6 c. bread flour

In a large bowl, dissolve the sugar in warm water, and then stir in yeast. Allow to proof until yeast resembles a creamy foam.

Mix salt and oil into the yeast. Mix in flour one cup at a time. Knead dough on a lightly floured surface until smooth (8-10 minutes or about 250 times). Place in a well-oiled bowl, and turn dough to coat. Cover with a damp cloth. Allow to rise until doubled in bulk, about 1 hour.

Punch dough down. Knead for a few minutes, and divide in half. Shape into loaves and place into two well-oiled 9 x 5 inch loaf pans. Allow to rise for 30 minutes, or until dough has risen 1 inch above pans.

Bake at 350°F for 30 minutes.

Basic Pizza Dough

Ingredients
- 1 c. warm water
- 1 package active dry yeast
- 2-1/2 c. all-purpose flour
- 2 T. olive oil
- 1/2 t. salt

Combine water and yeast in a large bowl. Add 1-1/2 c. flour and mix well. Add oil, salt and remaining flour. With clean hands, work the ingredients together until stiff dough forms. (Add last cup gradually—you may not need all of it.)

Knead dough on floured pastry cloth or board for 5 minutes or until shiny and elastic. Place dough into large mixing bowl that has been coated with olive oil; turn dough to coat it and cover with kitchen towel. Let dough rest for one hour in warm place until doubled in size.

Remove dough to lightly floured surface and split into two balls. Cover and let rest again for another 15 minutes. Dough can now be shaped into pizza crust. Top with cream soup substitute (page 40-41) and toppings. Bake at 400°F for 15 minutes.

Irish Soda Bread

From Interstitial Cystitis Network's IC Chef
www.ic-network.com/icchef/

Ingredients

- 2-1/2 c. whole wheat flour
- 1 c. all-purpose flour
- 2 T. sugar
- 1-1/2 t. baking soda
- 1 t. salt
- 4 T. butter, room temperature
- 1 egg
- 1-1/4 c. buttermilk, room temperature

Mix together all the dry ingredients in a large bowl. Using your fingertips, work the butter into the flour mixture until the mixture resembles breadcrumbs. Beat the egg and buttermilk in a separate bowl and gradually add to the flour mixture. Mix with a spoon at first, and then by hand or with mixer when the dough becomes stiff.

On a lightly floured work surface, thoroughly work the dough to blend all the ingredients. Do not knead. Sprinkle with flour if the dough should stick. Shape into a round ball and pat the top down slightly, and place on a greased or non-stick baking sheet. Cut a 1/2-inch deep cross in the top using a sharp knife or razor blade. Bake in 400°F oven for about 45 minutes, or until it has browned and the cuts have expanded. Remove from oven and cool on a wire rack before slicing.

Mozzarella Garlic Bread

Ingredients
- 1 loaf French bread
- 1/2 c. olive oil
- 1 t. parsley
- 1 t. dried basil
- 1/2 t. garlic salt
- 3/4 c. shredded mozzarella cheese

Preheat oven broiler. Cut bread in half lengthwise. Place on cookie sheets. Brush each half with oil. Sprinkle with parsley, basil and garlic salt. Top with mozzarella cheese. Broil 7 to 10 minutes until cheese is bubbly and begins to brown. Serve warm.

Basic Biscuits

Ingredients
- 2 c. sifted flour
- 2 t. baking powder
- 1/2 t. salt
- 4 T. butter or shortening
- Scant 3/4 c. milk

Preheat oven to 400°F. Sift flour; then measure into medium mixing bowl. Add baking powder and salt, and sift again. Cut in shortening or butter. Add milk 2 T. at a time, stirring until soft dough is formed.

Turn out on slightly floured board and lightly "knead" for 30 seconds, enough to shape. Do not over-knead. Roll 1/2-inch thick and cut with 2-inch floured biscuit cutter.

Bake on ungreased sheet for 12-15 minutes. Makes 12 biscuits.

Homemade Flour Tortillas

Recipe courtesy www.cooks.com

Ingredients

- 2 c. all-purpose flour
- 1-1/2 t. baking powder
- 1 t. salt
- 2 t. vegetable oil or non-hydrogenated lard
- 3/4 c. lukewarm milk

In a bowl, stir together the flour, baking powder, and salt. Add vegetable oil to the lukewarm milk and whisk briefly to incorporate. Gradually add the milk to the flour mixture, and using clean hands, work into sticky dough.

Turn dough out onto a surface dusted with flour and knead vigorously for about 2 minutes or until the dough is no longer sticky. Return dough to bowl, cover with a damp cloth and allow to rest for 10-20 minutes so that it will be easier to roll out.

Divide dough into 8 balls of equal size, cover them, and let them rest again for about 20 minutes. Avoid letting them touch, if you don't want them to stick together.

Dust a clean pastry board or working surface with flour. One at a time, remove each piece of dough. Press it out into a 5-inch circle. Using a flour-dusted rolling pin, roll out the tortilla from the center out until the tortilla measures a little less than 1/4 inch thick and is a 7- or 8-inch circle.

Transfer the tortilla to a dry preheated skillet or griddle. When the tortilla begins to blister, allow it to cook for 30 seconds. Flip it, and cook the other side the same way.

Remove tortilla, place it in on a clean paper towel, and cover loosely with foil. Repeat for remaining tortillas.

Homemade Bread Crumbs

Making bread crumbs is actually very easy. For regular bread crumbs, simply take stale (but not completely dried out) bread and put it in a blender or food processor. Don't over process.

For recipes that call for "dried breadcrumbs," place stale bread on cooking sheet and bake at 275°F for two to three hours, or until moisture is out of the bread. Process as above. Crumbs can be stored in air-tight containers for up to two weeks.

Variation: Homemade Croutons: Use stale bread cut into ½-inch to 1-inch squares. Place on baking pan; brush lightly with olive oil or melted butter. Season as desired. Try various combinations of salt, pepper, garlic salt, thyme, basil, rosemary, and oregano. Bake at 275°F until crisp.

Easy Corn Bread
Recipe Courtesy of Quaker Oats®

Ingredients
- 1–1/4 c. all-purpose flour
- 3/4 c. corn meal
- 1/4 c. sugar
- 2 t. baking powder
- 1/2 t. salt
- 1 c. skim milk
- 1/4 c. vegetable oil
- 2 egg whites or 1 egg, beaten

Heat oven to 400°F. Grease 8 or 9-inch square pan. Combine dry ingredients. Stir in milk, oil and egg, mixing just until dry ingredients are moistened.

Pour batter into prepared pan. Bake 20 to 25 minutes or until light golden brown and wooden pick inserted in center comes out clean. Serve warm.

Maple Syrup Cornbread

Adapted with permission of Vermont Only:
www.vtonly.com/recipes.html

Ingredients

- 1-1/8 c. cornmeal
- 1-1/8 c. whole wheat flour
- 3 t. baking powder
- 1/2 t. salt
- 1 egg, well beaten
- 1/2 c. maple syrup
- 3/4 c. milk
- 3 T. melted shortening

Preheat oven to 400°F. Mix dry ingredients in large mixing bowl. Add wet ingredients. Stir until well blended but do not beat. Pour into a shallow well greased pan (9" x 9" or larger). Bake for 20 minutes. Cut in squares and serve hot with butter.

Sweet Potato Dough Bread

Recipe courtesy Alicia's Recipes www.aliciasrecipes.com

Ingredients

- 1-1/2 c. all-purpose flour
- 2 t. baking powder
- 1 t. ground cinnamon
- 1/2 t. ground cloves
- 1/2 t. salt
- 1/4 t. ground nutmeg
- 2 eggs
- 1 c. packed brown sugar
- 1/2 c. vegetable oil
- 1 c. cooked, mashed sweet potato
- 1/2 c. currants or raisins, if tolerated

Preheat oven to 350°F. Lightly grease 9 x 5 inch or 8 1/2 x 4 1/2 inch loaf pan and set aside. In a large mixing bowl combine flour, baking powder, cinnamon, cloves, salt, and nutmeg; whisk lightly to blend. In a medium mixing bowl beat together eggs, brown sugar and oil on medium speed until creamy. Beat in sweet potato until just combined. Add sweet potato mixture to dry ingredients in two batches, beating on low speed for about 1 minute after each addition. Mix just until blended. Fold in currants or raisins. Pour batter into prepared pan. Bake for about 1 hour, or until a tester inserted in the center comes out clean. Cool cake in pan, or wire rack, for 15 minutes. Turn onto rack to finish cooling.

Zucchini Bread
Recipe courtesy Alicia's Recipes www.aliciasrecipes.com

Ingredients
- 3 eggs
- 1 c. oil
- 1–1/2 c. sugar
- 1 t. vanilla
- 2 c. peeled & grated zucchini
- 3 c. flour
- 1 t. salt
- 1 t. cinnamon
- 1 t. soda
- 1/4 t. baking powder
- 1/2 to 1 c. chopped nuts

Preheat oven to 325°F. Beat eggs; blend in oil, sugar and flavoring. Add zucchini. Sift flour with dry ingredients. Beat into first mixture. Fold in nuts. Bake for 60 to 75 minutes. Makes two loaves. Bread freezes well

Almond Pear Bread

Recipe courtesy MealsForYou www.mealsforyou.com

Ingredients

- 2 c. sugar
- 3/4 c. corn oil
- 3 eggs
- 3 c. flour, all purpose
- 1/2 t. baking powder
- 1 t. baking soda
- 1/2 t. salt
- 1 t. cinnamon
- 1/2 t. nutmeg
- 2 c. fresh grated peeled pears
- 1 c. chopped almonds
- 1/2 t. vanilla
- 1/2 t. almond flavoring

Preheat oven to 325°F. Cream sugar, oil; beat in eggs. Sift flour, baking powder, soda, salt, and spices. Add grated pears and beat on medium speed until well mixed. Mix in flavorings and almonds until well blended. Bake in 2 greased, floured 9 x 5 x 3 inch loaf pans for 1 hour and 10 minutes or until done to the touch. Makes 2 loaves.

Julie's Blueberry Muffins

Ingredients

- 1/2 c. butter, softened
- 1 c. sugar
- 2 eggs
- 2 c. flour
- 2 t. baking powder
- 1/2 t. salt
- 1/2 c. evaporated milk
- 1 t. vanilla
- 2 c. fresh or frozen blueberries

Preheat oven to 350°F. Cream butter and sugar. Add eggs and mix well. Add flour, baking powder, salt, milk and vanilla. Fold in fruit. Pile high in muffin tins, prepared with non-stick spray. Bake 25-30 minutes.

Crumb Cake

Ingredients
- 1-1/2 c. flour
- 1 c. packed light brown sugar
- 1-1/2 t. baking powder
- 1 t. cinnamon
- 1/2 t. salt
- 1/2 c. butter, slightly softened
- 1 egg, beaten
- 1/2 c. milk

Preheat oven to 375°F. Grease and flour an 8-inch square cake pan. Sift together flour, sugar, baking powder, cinnamon, and salt. Cut in butter until crumbly. Put 1/2 cup of mixture aside. Beat together egg and milk in small bowl; mix into remaining crumb mixture. Pour into prepared baking pan. Coarsely sprinkle coffeecake with 1/2 cup of reserved crumb mixture. Bake 30 to 35 minutes. Makes 12 servings.

Cinnamon Coffeecake Muffins

Recipe courtesy of Quaker® Oats

Topping Ingredients
- 1/4 c. Quaker® oats (quick or old fashioned, uncooked)
- 3 T. whole-wheat flour
- 2 T. granulated sugar
- 1/4 t. ground cinnamon
- 1 t. trans-fat free spread

Muffin Ingredients
- 3 T. + 1/2 c. granulated sugar, divided
- 1 T. ground cinnamon
- 1 c. Quaker® oats (quick or old fashioned, uncooked)
- 1 c. low fat buttermilk
- 1 egg, well beaten
- 1/4 c. canola oil
- 1/2 c. whole-wheat flour
- 1/2 c. all-purpose flour
- 1/4 c. original toasted wheat germ
- 1-1/2 t. baking powder
- 1/2 t. baking soda

Heat oven to 375°F. Spray bottoms only of 12 medium muffin cups with nonstick cooking spray.

For topping, combine all ingredients in small bowl; set aside.

For muffins, combine 3 tablespoons sugar and cinnamon in small bowl; set aside. In large bowl, combine oats and buttermilk; mix well. Let stand 5 minutes. Stir in egg and oil until blended.

In medium bowl, combine flours, wheat germ, baking powder, baking soda, and remaining 1/2 cup sugar; mix well. Add to oat mixture all at once; stir just until dry ingredients are moistened.

(Do not over mix.) Sprinkle cinnamon-sugar over top of batter; gently stir 4 to 5 times to make swirls.

Fill muffin cups almost full; sprinkle with topping. Bake 18 to 20 minutes or until light golden brown. Cool muffins in pan on wire rack 5 minutes; remove from pan. Serve warm. Makes 12 muffins.

Flaxseed Muffins
From www.goldenflax.com

Ingredients
- 1-1/2 c. all-purpose flour
- 1-1/2 c. ground flax seed
- 3/4 c. brown sugar
- 1 T. baking powder
- 3/4 t. nutmeg
- 1-1/2 t. cinnamon
- 2 c. milk
- 1 egg

Preheat oven to 350°F. Mix all ingredients; stir until well mixed. Spray muffin pan with cooking spray or use pan liners. Fill with batter until 3/4 full. Bake at 350°F for approx. 25-30 minutes. Makes 12 muffins.

Maple and Pear Scones

Adapted from Hannah's Kitchen: www.thatsmyhome.com

Ingredients Maple Pear Butter:

- 1 large, very ripe Bartlett pear, peeled, cored and mashed
- 1/4 c. soft butter (no substitutions)
- 1-1/2 T. pure maple syrup

Ingredients for Scones:

- 3 c. flour
- 1/3 c. sugar
- 2 t. baking powder
- 1 t. cinnamon
- 1/2 t. baking soda
- 1/4 t. salt
- 3/4 c. butter, cut into pieces
- 3/4 c. buttermilk
- 1 t. pure maple extract
- 1 c. peeled and diced Bartlett pears (about 1-1/2 medium pears)
- 1/2 c. chopped almonds
- 1/2 T. sugar (for topping)

To make maple pear butter, simmer mashed pear in a small saucepan over medium heat for about 15 minutes or until liquid has evaporated. (Pear will begin to stick to pan at this point.) Let cool slightly and stir in butter and maple syrup. Let stand at room temperature to thicken. (Butter can be prepared ahead, if desired, and stored in the refrigerator.)

To prepare scones, preheat oven to 400° F.

Combine flour, sugar, baking powder, cinnamon, baking soda, and salt in a medium bowl. Cut in butter with a pastry blender until butter is the size of peas (do not over blend). Stir in buttermilk, maple extract, pears and almonds. Turn mixture onto a lightly floured board and knead several times until dough is smooth.

Press into a 10-inch circle and cut into 10 wedges with a sharp knife. Place wedges 1-inch apart on a baking sheet lined with parchment paper. Sprinkle lightly with 1/2 tablespoon sugar. Bake for 20 minutes or until golden brown on top.

Serve warm with Maple Pear Butter. Makes 10 scones.

Main Dishes

Main Dishes

If you have a chronic illness, the tasks at the end of a day can often seem overwhelming. Fortunately, with a little bit of planning, balancing your evening activities does not mean you will have to give up home-cooked meals. Here are some ideas to get you started:

1. Plan your meals a week or even a month in advance. Create grocery lists based on your meals.

2. Take advantage of the days when you are feeling your best. Prepare double batches (or more) of a meal and freeze the extra to use on days when you are too busy or too tired to cook. Similarly, save time and energy by preparing two, three, or even four weeks of meals on one day.

3. Remember, simplicity is the rule when you don't feel well. Choose entrees with fewer than six ingredients.

4. Experiment with a slow cooker. Beef, chicken, and even turkey breasts can be simmered all day with potatoes and vegetables, gradually filling the house with a mouth-watering aroma. Hint: use the new slow cooker liners to make clean-up a breeze.

5. Check out Reynolds® Cooking Bags. This is similar to using a slow cooker: Just add meat, potatoes, vegetables and seasonings to the bag, place it in a baking pan, and pop the whole thing into the oven. Not only does your meal take care of itself, but there is little if any clean-up when your meal is finished.

6. Finally, don't be afraid to take some short cuts. Consider using pre-cut ingredients or purchasing salads from restaurants to take home to add to your meal. Boneless, skinless chicken breasts save time not only in preparation but also in cooking time.

Skillet Chicken Dinner

Ingredients
- 1 T. cooking oil
- 2 stalks celery, trimmed and sliced into 1-inch segments
- 1 medium onion
- 2 T. minced garlic
- 1/2 c. all purpose flour
- 1 t. salt
- Dash pepper, if tolerated
- 2 T. dried rosemary leaves, slightly crushed
- 4 boneless, skinless chicken breasts (can substitute pork chops trimmed to 1-inch thick)
- 4 medium potatoes, peeled and sliced
- 3 carrots, peeled and sliced into coins
- 1/2 c. homemade chicken stock
- 1 ½-c. water
- 2 T. cornstarch

Preheat electric skillet to 350°F. Heat oil in pan. Add celery, onion, and garlic, stirring until vegetables are transparent.

Combine flour, salt, pepper, and rosemary in medium mixing bowl. Coat chicken breasts or pork chops with flour mixture and place in hot oil. Cook 3 to 4 minutes until golden; then turn and brown on the other side. Add potatoes, carrots, and chicken stock to pan. Cover and simmer 25 to 30 minutes, checking frequently to add water if necessary. Meal is ready when chicken reaches 165°F or pork chops reach 160°F and vegetables are cooked through. Remove meat and vegetables. Add 1 cup of water to pan to deglaze, heating again to a simmer. Stir 1/2 c. water and starch in small bowl, whisking until smooth. Add starch mixture to pan; whisk together for gravy. Serves 4.

Egg Drop Chicken

From Interstitial Cystitis Network's IC Chef
www.ic-network.com/icchef/

Ingredients

- 1 lb. pounded chicken cutlets
- 1-1/2 qt. Egg Drop Soup (no MSG)
- 3 c. cooked white rice

Pound chicken cutlets, coat with flour, then dip in eggs. Pan fry in pure vegetable oil until cooked through. Pour Egg Drop Soup over chicken and let simmer for 20 minutes. Serve over rice.

Note: You can purchase Egg Drop Soup from your local Chinese Restaurant if they do not use MSG, or you can make your own:

- 1-1/2 qt. chicken stock
- 2-3 T. cornstarch (to thicken)
- 4-6 eggs

Bring chicken stock to full boil; add cornstarch to thicken. Then drop raw eggs one at a time into stock, breaking them up by constantly stirring as they cook. Serves 6.

Honey Sesame Chicken

From Interstitial Cystitis Network's IC Chef
www.ic-network.com/icchef/

Ingredients

- 4-6 pieces of chicken (thighs are best for this dish)
- 1/2 c. honey
- 1/4 c. sesame seeds
- Salt and freshly ground pepper to taste

Remove the skin from the chicken pieces if you want to reduce the fat content. Season with salt and pepper and place in a baking pan. A layer of aluminum foil underneath will make clean-up easier. Drizzle with honey and sprinkle a liberal amount of sesame seeds on each piece. Bake in a 325°F oven for 30 minutes, or until cooked through. Serves 4.

Italian Baked Chicken

From: *A Taste of the Good Life: A Cookbook for an Interstitial Cystitis Diet* by Beverley Laumann

Ingredients

- 2 chicken breast halves, skinless
- 1/3 c. unseasoned breadcrumbs
- 1/2 t. dried oregano
- 1/4 t. dried marjoram
- 1/8 t. salt
- 1/8 t. pepper
- 1 egg white, slightly whisked
- 3 T. margarine, melted

Rinse and dry chicken. Preheat oven to 375°F. In a bowl, combine breadcrumbs with oregano, marjoram, salt, and pepper. Roll chicken in egg white, then in the crumb mixture to coat. Pour the melted butter in shallow baking dish and turn chicken pieces in it to coat. Arrange pieces in baking dish, not touching, and bake at 375°F until tender, about 50 minutes. Do not turn. Lift out carefully from pan with spatula. Serves 2.

Grilled Chicken Kebabs

- 12 to 16 bamboo skewers
- 6 boneless, skinless chicken breasts cut into 1-inch cubes
- 1 green and 1 red bell pepper, cored, seeded, and cut into 1-inch square pieces
- 12 – 16 small cleaned mushroom caps
- 1/4 c. olive oil
- 1/4 c. pear juice
- 2 t. garlic powder
- 2 t. onion powder
- 2. t. dried rosemary leaves, crushed slightly
- 1 t. salt
- 1/2 t. pepper, if tolerated

Preparation: Soak skewers in water for at least 30 minutes. Arrange chicken pieces, peppers, and mushrooms on soaked skewers. In a small bowl, mix together the oil, pear juice, garlic powder, onion powder, salt, and black pepper. Place the kebabs in a 13 x 9 baking pan. Pour marinade over kebabs. Cover and refrigerate for a minimum of 30 minutes and up to 8 hours.

Grilling: Set gas grill to medium-high. Place the skewers of chicken on the hot grill and grill for 6 to 10 minutes, turning frequently, on an uncovered grill. Chicken pieces should reach a temperature of 165°F. Serve immediately over rice or pasta.

Grilled Steak Kebabs: Substitute 1-1/2 pounds round steak cut into 1-inch cubes for chicken.

Baked Chicken Nuggets

- 2 boneless chicken breasts or 3 boneless thighs
- 1 c. finely crushed bread crumbs
- 1/2 t. salt
- Dash pepper, if tolerated
- 1/2 t. dried basil
- 1/4 c. melted butter (to lower fat content, use 1/4 c. skim milk or buttermilk)

Preheat oven to 400° F. Cut chicken into 1-1/2 inch squares. Combine dry ingredients in small bowl. Dip chicken pieces in melted butter, then in crumb mixture. Pat crumbs on to coat. Place on baking sheet that has been sprayed with cooking spray. Bake for 10 minutes, remove from oven and turn nuggets. Bake for another 5 to 10 minutes until golden brown.

Rosemary Beef (serves one)

From Meals For You: www.mealsforyou.com

Ingredients

- 1/4 t. rosemary, crumbled or 1/2 t. fresh, minced
- 1/2 t. salt (optional)
- 1 t. pepper
- 1 clove garlic, minced
- 1 strip steak, about 1/4 lb. each
- 1-1/2 t. olive oil

Prepare grill or broiler. Mash rosemary, salt, pepper, and garlic together in a bowl. Rub mixture into meat and let sit about 15 minutes. Grill meat 3 minutes per side for medium-rare meat; cook longer as desired.

Lazy Sunday Roast Beef Dinner

Ingredients
- 3 to 4 pound beef roast, visible fat trimmed
- 4 medium potatoes, peeled and halved (can substitute sweet potatoes)
- 3 carrots, peeled and cut into 2-inch pieces
- 2 stalks of celery, cut into 1/2-inch pieces
- 1 medium onion, quartered, if tolerated
- 1/2 c. boiling water
- 1 T. minced garlic
- 1 t. salt
- 1/2 t. pepper, if tolerated
- 2 t. dried basil

It doesn't get any easier than this! Layer roast and vegetables in a 3 qt slow cooker. Add water. Sprinkle in garlic, salt, pepper, and basil. Cook on medium for 6 to 8 hours or on high for 4 to 6 hours. Temperature of roast at its center should be a minimum of 145°.

Variations:
- **Chicken Dinner:** Substitute 5 to 7 skinned chicken breasts or thighs for beef. Substitute rosemary for basil.
- **Turkey Dinner:** Substitute 4 to 5 pound turkey breast for beef. Substitute poultry seasoning for basil.
- **Beef Stew:** Cut up roast into 1-1/2 inch cubes. Increase water to 1-1/2 c. One hour before serving: Mix 2 T. flour with 1/2 c. warm water; stir until smooth. Stir gently into stew. Continue cooking for at least an hour.

No-Tomato Meatloaf

Ingredients

- 1 T. olive oil
- 1/2 small onion, finely chopped
- 1 chopped garlic clove (more if desired)
- 3/4 c. chopped mushrooms
- 1/4 c. fresh basil leaves, finely chopped
- 1 lb. ground beef
- 1 large egg
- 2 T. milk
- 4 to 6 T. breadcrumbs
- Freshly ground black pepper, if tolerated
- Salt to taste

Preheat oven to 425° F. Heat the oil in a small pan. Sauté onions; add garlic and cook 30 to 40 seconds. Add mushrooms and cook until brown. Add basil. Remove from heat and let cool slightly.

Combine this mixture with remaining ingredients in a bowl. (Adjust amount of breadcrumbs to create appropriate consistency for loaf.) Mold mixture into two small loaves. Place in ungreased 9 x 9 square pan, leaving about 2 inches between. Bake for 30 minutes.

May substitute 3/4 cup old-fashioned uncooked oatmeal for breadcrumbs.

Beef & Broccoli

- 1 lb. boneless sirloin steak
- 1 t. olive oil
- 1 clove garlic
- 2 c. broccoli florets
- 1/2 c. carrots, peeled and julienned
- 1 medium onion, if tolerated
- 1 1/2 c. Cream Soup Substitute (pg. 40)
- 1/4 cup water
- 2 t. molasses
- 1 t. orange zest
- 1 t. salt
- Dash pepper, to taste, if tolerated

Slice the beef into thin strips against the grain. Heat oil over medium heat in skillet or wok. Add the beef and garlic; cook until the beef is starting to brown. Toss in broccoli, carrots, and onion. Cook for additional 5 minutes.

Add soup substitute, water, molasses, zest, salt, and pepper and heat to boiling. Cover, reducing heat to low. Cook additional 5 minutes or until the vegetables are tender. Serve over rice. Serves 4.

Pear-Smothered Pork Chops

From: *A Taste of the Good Life: A Cookbook for an Interstitial Cystitis Diet* by Beverley Laumann

Ingredients
- 2 center-cut pork loin chops, about 3/4" thick
- 1/4 t. ground sage
- Dash salt and pepper
- 1 large, firm-ripe pear
- 2 T. flour
- 1 c. water

In a skillet, brown pork chops in vegetable oil, seasoning with salt and pepper if desired. Remove chops to casserole dish. Sprinkle sage on chops.

Peel and slice pear, placing slices on top of chops. In a small bowl, combine flour with 2 T. of water to make paste; then add remaining water and molasses and mix well. Over low heat, pour liquid into hot skillet, scraping up browned bits of pork. When slightly thickened, pour sauce over chops. Cover and bake at 350°F for 40 minutes, or until done.

Rosemary Salmon

Ingredients
- 4 6-oz. salmon steaks
- Salt and pepper, if tolerated, to taste
- 2 T. rosemary leaves
- 3 T. butter
- 4 T. honey

Preheat oven to 350°F.

Season flesh side of salmon with salt, pepper and rosemary. Melt butter in skillet. Place fish, flesh side down, in the pan for 5 minutes until salmon is browned.

Remove salmon from skillet, place in oven-safe pan. Pour honey over the salmon and bake 10 to 12 minutes or until steaks are done.

Linguine with Clam Sauce

From: *A Taste of the Good Life: A Cookbook for an Interstitial Cystitis Diet* by Beverley Laumann

Ingredients

- 3 cloves garlic, minced
- 1/4 c. olive oil
- 3 cans (6 oz.) chopped clams
- 8 oz. clam juice (bottled)
- 2 T. dried parsley
- 1/2 t. basil
- 1/4 t. salt
- 1/8 t. pepper
- 3 servings of hot, cooked linguine noodles (about 3 c.)

In medium saucepan sauté the garlic in olive oil until tender. Drain chopped clams, reserving liquid from two of the cans. Add reserved liquid, clam juice, parsley, basil, salt, and pepper to the garlic. Bring to boil; then reduce heat and simmer about 5 minutes.

Add chopped clams, heat through, and serve over linguine noodles (or your favorite hot cooked pasta).

Shrimp Variation: Omit one can of chopped clams and substitute 1/2 c. of tiny cooked cocktail shrimp.

Seared Scallops with Vanilla Sauce
Recipe courtesy of Nielsen-Massey Vanilla: www.nielsenmassey.com

Ingredients
- 1/2 lb. sea scallops
- 1/2 c. butter
- 1 cup cream
- 2 T. onion, minced
- 1 clove of garlic, minced
- 1/2 t. Nielsen-Massey Madagascar Bourbon Pure Vanilla Extract
- 1/2 lb. angel hair pasta, cooked
- Chopped parsley for garnish

Melt butter in a 12-inch frying pan. Add scallops and cook until just done, about one minute per side. Remove from pan and keep warm. Add onion and garlic to the pan and sauté 2 minutes. Add cream and vanilla. Cook and stir over medium heat until slightly thickened. Add scallops back to the pan and stir. Serve over pasta. Sprinkle with fresh parsley. Serves 2.

Vegetables

Vegetables

The vegetable food group is one of the easiest to work with if you have a restricted diet due to bladder symptoms. Keep broccoli, cauliflower, peas, green beans, carrots and corn in your freezer for quick side dishes. Canned vegetables can also be used; however, it is important to read labels for miscellaneous ingredients like MSG or other flavor enhancers.

Fresh vegetables are also becoming more convenient. Most markets sell ready-made vegetable trays, which can be a real time saver, not just for snacks and parties, but also for inclusion in recipes.

Microwave or steam vegetables to retain most of the nutrients. If you heat vegetables on a stove, use as little water as possible and consider reusing the cooking water in some way as a base for a soup or sauce. Season your vegetables with butter, olive oil, salt, pepper, and a variety of bladder-friendly herbs and spices like basil and rosemary. Here are a few recipes to get you started, but don't be afraid to experiment on your own.

Green Beans Almandine
Julie's Favorites

Ingredients
- 10 oz. bag frozen French-cut green beans
- 1 T. olive oil
- 1/2 c. almond slices or slivers
- 2 t. dried basil

Steam green beans over medium heat in ½ cup water. Drain off extra water. Drizzle olive oil over beans. Add almonds and basil; toss to season. Add salt and pepper to taste.

Peas and Mushrooms

Ingredients
- 10 oz. bag frozen baby peas
- 1/2 c. water
- 8 oz. can sliced mushrooms, drained
- 2 T. butter, softened
- Scant 1/2 t. sage (basil is also good)
- Salt to taste

Add peas and water to medium sauce pan and bring to a boil. Turn off heat and let rest 5 minutes to cook peas through. Drain water from peas. Fold in mushrooms, butter, sage, and salt. Reheat on low if necessary.

Microwave instructions: Put peas with 2 T. water in medium microwave-safe bowl (You do not need 1/2 c. of water to cook peas in the microwave.) Cover loosely, leaving room for steam to escape. Cook on high for 3 to 4 minutes. Fold in mushrooms, butter, and seasonings. Reheat 30 seconds.

Creamed Peas
From MealsForYou: www.mealsforyou.com

- 2 c. frozen green peas
- 1/3 oz. unsalted butter
- 1/8 t. salt, approximately
- 1/8 t. freshly ground black pepper, if tolerated

Place peas in a steamer basket over boiling water. Cover pan and steam 10 minutes or until bright green and tender. Drain and mash with a fork. Add butter and salt and pepper to taste. Stir to combine. Serve hot.

Creamy Carrots and Peas

From MealsForYou: www.mealsforyou.com

- 3/4 lb. carrots, thinly sliced
- 1/2 lb. green peas
- 1 t. unsalted butter
- 1 oz. cream cheese, room temperature, cut up
- 1/2 t. salt, or to taste
- 1/4 t. white pepper

Place carrots in a steamer basket over boiling water. Cover saucepan and steam 4 minutes. Add peas and steam 3-4 minutes or until peas are tender. Drain and return vegetables to saucepan. Add remaining ingredients and toss.

Maple Glazed Carrots

From Vermont Only: www.vtonly.com

- 8 medium carrots
- 3 T. butter
- 1/4 c. maple syrup
- 1/2 t. brown sugar

Slice carrots. Cook until tender. Melt butter. Add maple syrup and brown sugar. Simmer carrots in maple syrup mixture until glazed. (Try this on pork chops!)

Herbed Broccoli Bake

Adapted from MealsForYou: www.mealsforyou.com

- 1 lb. broccoli florets
- 2 t. unsalted butter
- 1/4 c. onions, chopped
- 1/2 c. celery, chopped
- 1/4 c. canned mushrooms, drained and chopped
- 1/2 c. water or vegetable stock
- 1/2 t. basil
- 1/2 t. oregano
- 1/2 c. plain breadcrumbs

Preheat oven to 350°F. Place broccoli in a steamer basket over boiling water. Cover and steam 4 to 5 minutes or until just tender. Drain and keep warm. Melt butter in a heavy nonstick skillet over medium heat. Sauté onions, celery, and mushrooms 4 to 5 minutes or until tender. Stir in water (or stock), basil, and oregano. Add salt and pepper to taste. Simmer another 2 minutes. Stir in broccoli. Transfer mixture to a lightly oiled baking dish. Top with breadcrumbs and bake 15 minutes.

Broccoli with Garlic and Mushrooms

From www.mealsforyou.com

Ingredients
- 1 oz. butter
- 2 cloves garlic, crushed
- 4 mushrooms, sliced
- 12 oz. broccoli, cut into small florets

Heat butter and garlic in a heavy nonstick pan over medium high heat. Add mushrooms. Cook over medium heat 2 minutes or until tender. Remove from pan; set aside. Add broccoli and stir-fry for 3 or 4 minutes until tender. Return mushrooms to pan; stir until heated through. Serve hot.

Corn and Broccoli Casserole

Adapted with permission from Alicia's Recipes:
www.aliciasrecipes.com

Ingredients

- 1 can (16 oz.) cream style corn
- 1 pkg. (10 oz.) frozen chopped broccoli, thawed
- 1/2 c. crushed saltines, divided
- 1 egg, beaten
- 1 T. dried minced onion
- Dash pepper
- 2 T. butter or margarine, melted

Combine corn, broccoli, 1/4 cup of saltines, egg, onion, and pepper in a large bowl. Place in a greased 1-1/2 quart baking dish. Combine the butter and remaining saltines; sprinkle over top. Cover and bake at 350°F for 45 minutes. Makes 6 servings.

Creamed Corn

- 1/2 medium onion, finely chopped, if tolerated
- 2 T. butter
- 2-1/2 c. fresh corn
- 1 teaspoon sugar
- 1/2 cup heavy cream (may substitute 1/2 c. evaporated skim milk)
- salt and pepper if tolerated, to taste

In a large frying pan, sauté onion in butter until transparent. Stir in corn, sugar, and cream. Stir constantly, heating until mixture reaches a boil; then reduce heat. Continue to stir while mixture simmers for about 10 minutes. Serves 5 to 6.

Microwave Corn on the Cob
Instructions courtesy of Linda Schuessler

Wash up to four ears of corn, lopping the ends off and removing any visibly soiled husks. Place ears in a circle on a paper towel; microwave on high for approximately 2 minutes per ear. When you shuck the cooked ears to serve, the silk removes quite easily with the husk. Alternately, you can pull the husks back, remove the silk, butter the corn, then pull the husk over the cob, fastening with a rubber band before cooking. Both of the above methods yield a moist, tender ear of corn.

Butternut Squash and Red Pepper Casserole
Adapted from MealsForYou: www.mealsforyou.com

- 2-1/4 lbs. butternut squash, peeled, seeded and cut into 1-inch cubes
- 3/4 large red bell pepper, seeded and cut into 1-inch pieces
- 2 t. olive oil
- 2 large cloves garlic, crushed
- 2 T. fresh parsley, minced
- 1 t. fresh rosemary leaves, minced
- Salt and pepper to taste
- 4 T. toasted bread crumbs

Preheat oven to 400°F. Combine squash, pepper, oil, garlic, parsley, and rosemary in a bowl. Season with salt and freshly ground black pepper to taste. Transfer mixture to a gratin dish or other shallow baking dish and sprinkle evenly with bread crumbs. Bake about 1 hour in middle of oven until squash is tender and top is golden

Vanilla-Scented Butternut Squash Risotto

Adapted with permission of The Vanilla.COMpany (www.vanilla.com)

Ingredients

- 2 T. extra-virgin olive oil
- 1/4 c. scallions, sliced thinly or
- 1/4 c. shallots finely chopped
- 1-1/2 c. Arborio or other medium grain rice
- 1/2 c. chopped parsley
- 3-1/2 c. butternut squash, peeled and cut into small chunks or bite-size pieces
- 5 c. chicken or vegetable broth
- 2 T. butter
- 1 t. pure vanilla extract (or more to taste)
- 1/2 c. crumbled feta cheese, as tolerated
- Freshly ground black pepper and salt to taste

In a heavy-bottomed pan, cook scallions or shallots in oil over low-medium heat until lightly golden (about 5 minutes). Add rice and turn several times to coat with oil. Increase the heat to medium-high, and add a ladle of broth, stirring constantly to keep rice from sticking to the bottom or sides of pan. When the broth has been absorbed, add another ladleful of broth, the squash, and the parsley. Stirring steadily to keep the rice from sticking, add the remainder of the broth, a ladleful at a time. The rice is done when it is firm, but tender, and without a chalky center.

Remove from the heat and add the butter, vanilla, cheese, salt, and a liberal amount of black pepper. Stir quickly to combine the ingredients. Serves 4-6

Spaghetti Squash

Adapted from MealsForYou: www.mealsforyou.com

- 1 spaghetti squash, cut into quarters and seeds discarded
- 1 T. plus 1 t. unsalted butter
- 1 clove garlic, crushed
- 1 T. basil, chopped
- 1 T. parsley, chopped

Place squash in a steamer basket cut side down over boiling water. Cover saucepan and steam 40 minutes or until squash is tender. (To microwave, cover squash pieces with plastic wrap. Place in a shallow casserole dish and microwave on high 15 minutes, turning halfway through cooking. Remove squash from oven and let stand 10 minutes.) Melt butter in a heavy nonstick skillet over medium low heat. Sauté garlic for 2 minutes. Scoop out squash from shell with a fork into a bowl, pulling into strands. Pour garlic butter over squash and toss. Sprinkle with basil and parsley; season with pepper to taste.

Baked Butternut Squash

Peel and cube 1 butternut squash. In medium saucepan, combine squash and enough water to cover, plus 2 inches. Heat to a boil, cooking until very soft. Remove from heat, drain off water, and mash. Add 1/4 c. butter, 3 T. brown sugar, and salt to taste. Bake in oven-proof serving dish at 350°F for 20 minutes.

Summary Stir-Fry

Ingredients

- 1 lb. fresh summer (yellow crook-neck) squash
- 1 lb. fresh zucchini
- 3 T. olive oil
- 1/2 medium onion, sliced and separated into strips
- 1/2 t. minced garlic
- 1/2 c. shredded carrot
- Salt and pepper if tolerated, to taste

Wash and slice squash and zucchini into strips. (You may prefer to cut into "coins.") Heat oil in large wok or frying pan, being careful not to over-heat or burn. Add garlic and onion, stirring and cooking until browned and transparent. Add squash and zucchini, cooking about 7 to 8 minutes until tender. Stir in shredded carrots, cooking an additional 4 to 5 minutes. Season with salt and pepper, if desired.

Hint: Other vegetables work well in this recipe too. Try mushrooms, colorful bell pepper strips, fresh yellow or green beans, or even small sections of corn on the cob!.

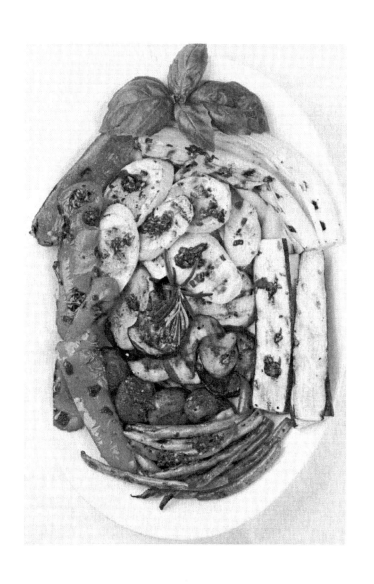

Potatoes, Pasta,
& Rice

Potatoes, Pasta, and Rice

Although potatoes, pasta, and rice by themselves are not usually an issue with interstitial cystitis and overactive bladder patients, sometimes the ingredients we use to make them fancy can be. You may be wondering, *"How can I enjoy a baked potato without sour cream, or pasta without tomato sauce?"* Well, in this section you will find many ways to dress up your starches without challenging your sensitive bladder.

Rosemary Red Potatoes

Ingredients
- 6 medium red-skin potatoes, cut in half
- 2 T. olive oil
- 1 T. rosemary leaves, slightly crushed
- 1/4 t. finely grated lemon zest
- Salt and pepper, if tolerated, to taste

Boil potatoes in medium sauce pan until soft, but not mushy. Drain and add potatoes back to pan. Combine olive oil, rosemary, and lemon zest in small bowl; drizzle over potatoes and toss lightly to coat. Season with salt and pepper if desired. Serves 4.

Potato Pancakes

Ingredients
- 4 large or 6 medium raw potatoes, grated
- 2 eggs, well beaten
- 1 t. salt
- 1/2 t. baking powder
- 1/4 c. flour
- 1/8 t. pepper
- 1 small onion, grated

Peel potatoes; grate potatoes into bowl of ice water. Drain liquid. Add beaten eggs; mix with rest of the ingredients. Drop by spoonfuls on hot oiled pan. Brown on both sides. Drain on paper towels. Serve with applesauce or sour cream or both. 4 servings.

Oven Fries

Adapted from *Food Allergy Survival Guide*
By Vesanto Melina, Jo Stepaniak, and Dina Aronson

Ingredients
- 2 large russet potatoes
- 1 T. olive oil (optional)
- 1/2 t. basil or 1/2 t. rosemary
- 1/4 t. salt
- Dash each: pepper, garlic powder, turmeric (optional)

Preheat the oven to 450°F. Spray large baking pan with cooking spray and set aside. Scrub the potatoes well and remove any eyes and discolored areas. Peeling is optional.

Cut into wedges or french-fry shapes. Place in a large bowl, sprinkle with the oil, if using, and toss to coat evenly. Sprinkle with the seasonings and toss again so all pieces are evenly coated. Arrange in a single layer on the prepared baking sheet. Bake until golden brown and fork tender, about 30 minutes. For more even browning, turn over once midway through the cooking cycle.

Nutrition Note: These thick, oven-baked French fries are low in fat but resonate with fabulous flavor. Potatoes provide a variety of minerals and are high in vitamin C, even after baking.

Miraculous Microwave Baked Potatoes

Pretty much everyone knows that they can clean a large russet potato, put it in the oven for an hour and they have a delicious baked potato. But did you know you could shorten the process significantly in the microwave?

Simply place your cleaned potato on a paper towel, poke it several times with a fork and cook on high heat in the microwave for 5 minutes. (This works best in microwaves that have an automatic rotating plate.) Let rest for 5 minutes to complete cooking and *voila*—you have a baked potato!

Do you need to cook more than one potato? The thing to remember is that a microwave cooks from the outside of a product to the inside:

For two potatoes, place side by side, cook on high 4 minutes. Then turn each potato so that the sides that were next to the other potato are now toward the outside. Cook another 3 to 4 minutes. Let rest 5 minutes to complete cooking.

For three to five potatoes, place potatoes end to end in a circle. For example, if you are cooking three potatoes, your potatoes will loosely resemble a triangle. Cook on high for 5 to 7 minutes (more minutes for more potatoes). Check the outside part of the potatoes with a fork. You should be able to pierce the skin, yet still meeting with slight resistance. Turn potatoes so that the undercooked side is toward outside. Cook on high for another 5 to 7 minutes. Let rest 5 minutes to complete cooking.

Top your baked potato with one or more of the following:
- Butter
- Cottage cheese
- Yogurt (drained of liquid)
- Mozzarella cheese
- Herb-infused oils
- Chives
- Broccoli
- Homemade and Healthy Ranch Dressing (pg. 57)
- Buttermilk Basil Dressing (pg. 56)
- Salt, pepper, or any herbs, spices that you can tolerate!

Variation: Try microwaving sweet potatoes or yams, which are loaded with vitamins A and C! Sweet potatoes and yams cook a bit faster, so reduce time and check occasionally for doneness.

Sweet Potato Oven Fries
My daughter Carolyn love these fries drizzled with a little honey!

Ingredients
- 4 medium sweet potatoes or yams
- 1/4 c. olive oil
- Sea salt to taste

Heat oven to 400°F. Wash, peel and slice potatoes into strips. In large bowl, toss cut potatoes with 1/4 cup oil to coat evenly. Arrange in single layer on baking sheet; bake until golden on bottom, about 15 minutes. Turn potatoes and bake another 10 to 15 minutes until browned. Remove from oven; transfer to absorbent paper to drain.

Bulgarian Potatoes

Ingredients

- 2 c. cottage cheese
- 1 stick (1/2 cup) melted unsalted butter
- 1 t. salt
- 3/4 t. black pepper
- 6 medium baking potatoes (wash potatoes, peel if desired)
- 2 large eggs
- 1 c. plain whole-milk yogurt (or 1/2 c. evaporated whole milk)

Preheat oven to 375°F. Butter 13 x 9 inch baking dish.

Blend cottage cheese in a food processer or blender until smooth—about 1 minute. Add butter, salt, and pepper and blend again until combined well. Cut potatoes into very thin slices. Spread one-third of potatoes evenly in one layer in dish and top with one-third of the cottage cheese mixture (mixture will not cover potatoes completely). Proceed by alternating layers of potatoes and the cottage cheese mixture, topping with cottage cheese mixture. Cover with foil and bake until potatoes are tender, 60 to 70 minutes.

Combine eggs and yogurt (or milk) in a bowl. Pour egg mixture evenly over potatoes and bake, uncovered, until custard is set, about 20 minutes.

No Cheese Pesto Sauce

Ingredients
- 3 c. fresh basil leaves
- 1 c. fresh parsley sprig
- 4 garlic cloves, crushed
- 4 T. olive oil
- 3 T. toasted pine nuts
- Pepper, if tolerated, to taste

Use food processor to chop basil and parsley. Add garlic and olive oil; process another 20 seconds. Add pine nuts and finish processing. Use as topping for pasta or baked potatoes, or as a garnish for chicken.

No Cheese "Alfredo" Sauce for Pasta

Ingredients
- 1/4 c. olive oil
- 2 T. flour
- 2 cans evaporated skim milk
- 1 t. minced garlic
- 1 t. minced onion
- 3 T. fresh basil, finally chopped
- 1/2 t. salt
- Pepper, if tolerated, to taste

Heat oil in saucepan over medium heat. Add flour, whisking until smooth. Add remaining ingredients, whisking until sauce has thickened. Use as a topping for pasta or baked potatoes, or as a garnish for chicken.

Variations:
- Add 3/4 c. cooked chicken breast, cubed
- Add 1 c. steamed broccoli florets and 1/4 c. red bell pepper, finely chopped

Barley Pilaf with Mushrooms
From MealsForYou: www.mealsforyou.com

Ingredients
- 1 T. plus 1 t. olive oil
- 2 c. onion, chopped
- 1/2 lb. mushrooms, thinly sliced
- 1 bay leaf
- 1 c. pearl barley
- 2 c. water
- 3 T. fresh parsley, minced

Heat oil in a heavy saucepan over medium heat. Sauté onion, mushrooms and bay leaf 5 minutes, stirring until onion is softened. Stir in barley, water, and salt and pepper to taste. Bring to a boil. Reduce heat to low, cover pan and simmer 30-35 minutes, or until liquid is absorbed and barley is tender. Discard bay leaf and stir in parsley. Fluff with a fork before serving.

Long Grain Rice with Peas
From www.mealsforyou.com

Ingredients
- 1 c. chicken stock (no MSG)
- 1 c. water
- 1 c. long grain rice
- Dash of salt and pepper (optional)
- 1-1/2 c. frozen peas, thawed
- 1 T. unsalted butter or margarine

Combine stock and water in a saucepan over medium high heat. Stir in rice, salt, and pepper to taste and bring to a boil. Immediately reduce heat to low. Cover and simmer 15 minutes. Add peas to rice without stirring. Cover and simmer 5 minutes or until rice is tender and liquid is absorbed. Remove from heat and let sit 5 minutes. Add butter and fluff with a fork. Serves 4.

Almond Rice

Ingredients
- 1 c. chicken stock
- 1 c. water
- 1 c. long grain white rice
- 2 T. slivered almonds
- 1/8 t. salt (optional)

Bring stock and water to a boil in a saucepan over high heat. Stir in remaining ingredients and pepper to taste and return to a boil. Immediately reduce heat to low. Cover saucepan and simmer 20-25 minutes or until rice is tender and liquid is absorbed.

Rosemary Red Ribbon Rice
From *Food Allergy Survival Guide*
By Vesanto Melina, Jo Stepaniak, and Dina Aronson

Ingredients
- 1-1/2 c. vegetable stock or water
- 1/2 c. raisins (preservative free)
- 1 t. crushed garlic
- 1/2 t. salt
- 1/4 to 1/2 t. dried rosemary, well crumbled
- 1 c. white basmati rice
- 1 small red bell pepper, sliced into matchsticks (omit if sensitive to red peppers; many IC patients are not)
- 1/2 c. coarsely chopped almonds
- 1 T. extra-virgin olive oil

Combine the water, raisins, garlic, salt, and rosemary in a saucepan and bring to a boil. Stir in the rice, cover, and reduce the heat to low. Cook until almost all the liquid has been absorbed, about 18 to 20 minutes. Remove from the heat, add the bell pepper, almonds, and oil; Toss gently with a fork until evenly distributed. Cover and let stand for 5 to 10 minutes. Serves 6.

Black-Eyed Peas and Green Beans
Adapted from Alicia's Recipes: www.aliciasrecipes.com

Ingredients
- 1 lb. black-eyed peas
- 1 clove garlic, peeled and crushed
- Salt and pepper if tolerated, to taste
- 2 qts. water
- 1 lb. fresh green beans

Soak black-eyed peas overnight, drain. Add 2 quarts water, garlic, salt, and pepper. Simmer for 3 hours until done. Steam fresh green beans in a steamer or cook in 2 quarts water for about 1 hour. Add cooked green beans to black-eyed peas. Serves 8.

Simple Red Beans and Rice
From www.mealsforyou.com

Ingredients

- 1 c. chicken stock or vegetable stock
- 1 c. water
- 1/8 t. salt (optional)
- 1 c. white rice
- 1/2 lb. canned kidney beans, rinsed and drained
- 1 T. unsalted butter or margarine

Combine stock, water, and salt in a saucepan and bring to a boil over high heat. Stir in rice and return to a boil. Immediately reduce heat to low. Cover saucepan and simmer 15 minutes. Stir in beans. Cover and simmer another 5-8 minutes or until rice is tender and liquid is absorbed. Remove from heat and let stand 5-10 minutes. Add butter and fluff with a fork before serving.

Old-Fashioned Vermont Beans

Adapted with permission of Vermont Only:
www.vtonly.com/recipes.htm

Ingredients

- 2 lbs. dried navy beans
- 1/2 lb. cubed salt pork, if tolerated (May substitute cubed cooked pork or turkey.)
- 1 medium onion, cut into quarters
- 1/2 c. brown sugar
- 1 c. maple syrup
- 2 t. dry mustard
- 1/2 t. pepper (if tolerated)
- 2 t. salt
- 2 c. boiling water

Preheat oven to 350°F when ready to bake. Soak dried beans overnight and precook. Line the bottom of a bean pot or casserole with half the cubed meat followed by the onion. Add cooked beans. Mix together remaining ingredients and pour over beans. If necessary, add more water to cover. Top with remaining meat. Bake 5 to 6 hours, adding more boiling water and syrup, if liquid is needed.

Desserts & Candies

Desserts & Candies

All meals deserve a sweet ending, but when you can't have chocolate, lemon, and many fruits, your choices may seem limited as you try to satisfy that sweet tooth. The selection of desserts gets even slimmer for some bladder patients who cannot tolerate all of the ingredients used in many prepackaged desserts or dessert mixes.

On the other hand, most people would agree that nothing quite compares to a homemade dessert. Why would you have store-bought chocolate chip cookies made with mystery ingredients when you could have homemade oatmeal cookies made with yummy butterscotch chips? Or how many people would choose a pre-packaged chocolate pudding when they could have homemade rice pudding or crème brulee? So, yet again, here is an example of something being "taken away," while something better is being offered in its place.

So get ready to dust off that mixer and dig out your mixing bowls, because you are in for a real "treat."

Broiled Pears (serves 4)
Recipe courtesy MealsForYou: www.mealsforyou.com

Ingredients
- 4 pears, cut in half lengthwise and cored
- 1 T. plus 1 tsp. water
- 1/4 cup brown sugar
- 1 T. plus 1 t. unsalted butter

Arrange pears in a shallow broiler pan and brush with water. Sprinkle with brown sugar and dot with butter. Turn on broiler. Broil pears for 3-4 minutes or until sugar is bubbly.

Maple Pear Crunch (serves 4)
From www.mealsforyou.com

Ingredients
- 1/3 cup maple syrup
- 1 T. water
- 4 large ripe firm pears, cored and thinly sliced
- 1/2 c. all purpose flour
- 3 T. yellow cornmeal
- 3 T. brown sugar, packed
- 1/8 t. ground cinnamon
- 1/4 c. unsalted butter, chilled and cut into small pieces

Preheat oven to 375°F. Combine maple syrup and water in a heavy non-reactive saucepan (copper, aluminum, stainless steel, iron). Cook over low heat 5 minutes or until very hot. Remove from heat. Stir in pear slices and transfer to a buttered baking dish. Set aside. Combine next 4 ingredients in a food processor or bowl. Add butter and cut into dry ingredients until mixture resembles coarse meal. Sprinkle topping over pears and bake 40 minutes, or until bubbly and golden.

Blueberry and Pear Cobbler

Ingredients
- 1 lb. canned blueberries, drain and reserve half syrup
- 1 lb. canned pears, drained
- 1-1/2 cups self-rising flour
- 1/4 cup sugar
- 1/4 lb. butter
- 1 egg, beaten
- 1/3 cup milk

Place pears in a deep pie dish; add the blueberries and syrup. Mix flour and 1/4 c. sugar. Rub in margarine and add enough milk to make a soft dough. Spoon dough over fruit and sprinkle with extra sugar. Bake at 350°F for 35 to 40 minutes, until golden brown. Serve hot, with whipped cream.

Blueberry Cream Pie

Used with permission from Alicia's Recipes: www.aliciasrecipes.com

Ingredients
- 1 c. sour cream
- 2 T. flour
- 3/4 c. sugar
- 1 t. vanilla
- 1/4 t. salt
- 1 egg, slightly beaten
- 2-1/2 c. blueberries
- 1 deep dish 9" unbaked pie shell

Combine first six ingredients and beat 5 minutes at medium speed or until smooth. Fold in berries. Pour into shell and bake at 400°F for 25 minutes. For topping, combine 3 tablespoons flour, 3 tablespoons butter and 3 tablespoons chopped almonds. Remove pie from oven and sprinkle topping over pie. Bake an additional 10 minutes. Chill before serving.

Mini Blueberry Cheesecakes

Julie's Favorites

Ingredients
- 24 cupcake liners
- 24 vanilla wafers
- 2 pkg. softened cream cheese
- 3/4 c. sugar
- 2 eggs
- 1/2 t. lemon extract, if tolerated
- 1 t. vanilla extract
- 1 can blueberry pie filling
- Fresh sweetened whipped cream, if desired

Preheat oven to 375°F. Line cupcake pans with 24 cupcake liners. Place a vanilla wafer in bottom of each liner. Beat cream cheese, sugar, eggs, lemon extract, and vanilla in small bowl until fluffy.

Spoon cream cheese mixture into liners until about 1/2 full. Bake in preheated over for 15 to 18 minutes or until set. Chill. Top each cheesecake with spoonful of filling and top with whipped cream if desired. Makes 24.

Philadelphia Brand® Cheesecake
Used with permission from Kraft® Foods

Crust Ingredients
- 1 cup graham cracker crumbs
- 2 T. butter or margarine

Filling Ingredients
- 2 8-oz packages Philadelphia Brand Cream Cheese®, softened
- 1/2 c. sugar
- 1/2 t. lemon extract, if tolerated
- 1 t. grated lemon rind, if tolerated
- 1/2 t. vanilla extract
- 2 eggs, separated

Preheat oven to 325°F. Combine crumbs and margarine; press onto bottom of 9-inch springform pan. Bake at 325°F for 10 minutes. Lower oven temperature to 300°F.

Combine cream cheese, sugar, extracts, and rind—mixing at medium speed with electric mixer until well blended. Add egg yolks, one at a time, mixing well after each addition. Fold in stiffly beaten egg whites; pour over crust. Bake at 300°F for 45 minutes. Serve with fresh blueberries if desired. Serves 12.

Grandma Mary's Creamy Rice Pudding

Julie's mom made the BEST rice pudding!

Ingredients
- 1/2 c. uncooked rice (not instant type)
- 1/2 t. salt
- 1/4 c. sugar
- 1/4 t. cinnamon
- 2 1/2 c. milk (skim works well)

Combine all ingredients in large sauce pan. Cook on medium heat uncovered until rice is tender and milk is almost absorbed (45 to 60 minutes). Serve warm.

Easy Rice Pudding

Julie's Favorites

Ingredients
- 4 c. cooked rice (can be left over from meal)
- 1 egg
- 1/2 c. skim milk
- 1 t. vanilla
- 3/4 c. sugar
- 1/2 t. cinnamon, if tolerated

Break egg into medium bowl and beat until smooth. Add milk and vanilla; continue beating. Combine rice, sugar, (cinnamon) and liquid ingredients in medium saucepan. Continuously stir ingredients over medium heat, simmering for 5 minutes. Be careful not to burn. Remove from heat. Pudding can be enjoyed warm or cold!

Vanilla Crème Brûlée

Published with permission of www.VanillaShop.com

Ingredients

- 2 c. milk
- 1 vanilla bean or 1 t. pure ground vanilla
- 6 egg yolks
- 2 c. heavy cream
- 1-1/2 c. vanilla sugar*

Preheat oven to 400°F. Grease 6 custard cups with butter or vegetable oil spray. In microwave, bring milk to a boil. Remove. Add vanilla bean or pure ground vanilla; cover and let infuse for 20 minutes.

Beat eggs with sugar until creamy. Add infused milk, cream and whisk. Fill custard cups 3/4 full. Place the custard cups in a roasting pan; add 1 inch hot water to roasting pan.

Bake for 10 to 15 minutes (10 minutes for a smooth custard). Remove from oven and cool at room temperature. Before serving, sprinkle vanilla sugar on top and broil in oven. Serve at once. Makes 6 servings.

*Vanilla sugar can be purchased through the Vanilla Shop (www.vanillashop.com) or you can make your own by splitting vanilla beans and adding them to a covered storage container of sugar. The sugar can be stored indefinitely, replenished with fresh sugar or additional vanilla beans as necessary.

Maple Oatmeal Bars

Ingredients
- 2/3 c. flour
- 2/3 t. baking powder
- 1/2 t. salt
- 1/2 c. almonds, if tolerated
- 1/4 c. softened shortening
- 1/4 c. softened butter
- 1/2 c. sugar
- 1/2 c. maple syrup
- 1 t. vanilla
- 1 egg, slightly beaten
- 1 c. quick-cooking oatmeal

Sift together flour, baking powder, and salt; combine with chopped almonds and set aside. Cream together shortening, butter, and sugar. Blend in maple syrup, vanilla, and egg. Add sifted flour and almond mixture to the batter. Stir in oatmeal and mix well.

Spread in greased 9 x 9 inch cake pan. Bake in an oven heated to 350°F for 35 minutes. Let cool slightly, cutting into squares while still warm. Makes 12 to 16 bars.

Pam's No Bake Cookies
Special thanks to Pam

Ingredients
- 2 c. sugar
- 1/2 c. evaporated milk (skim evaporated milk is okay)
- 1/2 c. butter or low trans-fat margarine
- 3 c. old-fashioned oats
- 1/2 c. peanut butter
- 1 t. vanilla

Heat sugar, milk, and butter, bringing it to a slow boil for 2 minutes. Remove from heat. Stir in oats, peanut butter, and vanilla. Mix thoroughly and drop by teaspoonfuls on wax paper. Makes 24 cookies.

Quaker's® Famous Oatmeal Cookies
Published with permission of The Quaker Oats Company

Ingredients
- 1 c. firmly packed brown sugar
- 3/4 c. vegetable shortening
- 1/2 c. granulated sugar
- 1 egg
- 1/4 c. water
- 1 t. vanilla
- 3 c. uncooked Quaker® Oats (I prefer the old fashioned kind)
- 1 c. all-purpose flour
- 1 t. salt
- 1/2 t. baking soda

Heat oven to 350°F. In large bowl, beat brown sugar, shortening and granulated sugar until creamy. Add egg, water and vanilla; beat well. Add combined oats, flour, salt and baking soda; mix well.

Drop dough by rounded teaspoonfuls onto ungreased cookie sheets. Bake 11 to 13 minutes or until edges are golden brown. Remove to wire cooling rack. Cool completely. Store tightly covered. **Variation**: Add 3/4 c. butterscotch chips!

Crunchy Cookies

From Interstitial Cystitis Network's IC Chef
www.ic-network.com/icchef/

Ingredients

- 1 c. butter
- 1 c. brown sugar
- 1 c. granulated sugar
- 2 eggs
- 2 t. vanilla
- 2 c. unsifted flour
- 1 t. baking powder
- 1 t. baking soda
- 1 t. salt
- 2-2/3 c. coconut
- 3 c. corn flake cereal

Cream the butter and sugars together. Add the eggs and vanilla and mix well. In a separate bowl, combine the flour with the baking powder, baking soda, and salt. Add the flour mixture to the butter/sugar mixture. Mix well. Lastly, add the corn flake cereal and coconut and mix well. Drop by teaspoonfuls on a greased cookie sheet. Bake at 350°F for 12 minutes. Cookies will look slightly underdone, but they brown a little after being taken from the oven. Make sure you take them from the oven before they look done; in other words, don't over bake! Makes 36 cookies.

Low-Fat Oatmeal Blondies
From www.mealsforyou.com

Ingredients
- 1 c. all purpose flour
- 1 t. ground ginger
- 1 t. ground cinnamon
- 1/2 t. baking soda
- 1/8 t. ground cloves
- 1-1/2 c. quick cooking oats, uncooked
- 3/4 c. brown sugar, firmly packed
- 3/4 c. pitted dates
- 1/2 c. boiling water
- 1/4 c. unsalted butter
- 1 egg
- 2 egg whites
- 2 t. vanilla extract
- 1 c. powdered sugar, sifted
- 2 T. milk
- 1/2 t. vanilla extract

Preheat oven to 375°F. Sift together first 5 ingredients in a bowl and stir in oats. In a food processor, combine brown sugar and dates. Process until dates are finely chopped. Add boiling water and butter. Process until mixture is smooth. Add egg, egg whites, and vanilla to date mixture. Process to blend. Transfer date mixture to flour mixture. Mix thoroughly by hand. Lightly butter a 9 x 13 inch baking dish. Transfer mixture to baking dish. Bake 18-20 minutes, or until tester comes out clean when inserted in center. Transfer to a wire rack to cool 5 minutes. Combine powdered sugar, milk, and vanilla in a bowl. Mix thoroughly. Spread frosting over bars. Cool completely before serving. Serves 18.

Snicker Doodles

Ingredients

- 1 c. (2 sticks) butter
- 2 eggs
- 1 t. soda
- 1 t. vanilla
- 1-1/2 c. sugar
- 2-3/4 c. flour

Beat ingredients together. Form small balls and coat in mixture of 1 teaspoon cinnamon and 1 cup sugar. Place on cookie sheet. Bake at 375°F for 10 minutes. Makes 3 dozen.

Aunt Dorothy's Sugar Cookies

Sift together:

- 2-1/2 c. flour
- 1/2 t. baking soda
- 3/4 t. salt

Cream together until fluffy:

- 1/2 c. margarine or butter
- 1/2 c. trans-fat free shortening
- 1 c. sugar
- 1 t. vanilla
- 1 egg

Combine dry ingredients with wet, stirring until mixture is smooth. Blend in 2 T. of milk.

Roll dough into small balls. Place balls of dough 2 inches apart on ungreased cookie sheet. Press down with glass dipped in sugar. Bake at 375°F for 6 to 8 minutes.

Mom's Christmas Sugar Cookies

What great childhood memories I have of rolling and decorating these cookies with my mom and brothers. Why keep them just for Christmas? Cookie cutters are available for nearly every holiday!

Ingredients

- 1 c. sugar
- 1/4 c. shortening
- 1/2 c. butter
- 1/2 t. vanilla or almond flavoring
- 2 eggs
- 2-1/2 c. sifted flour
- 1 t. baking powder
- 1 t. salt

Pre-heat oven to 400°F. Cream sugar with shortening and butter until fluffy. Beat in vanilla and eggs. Add dry ingredients and beat into firm dough. Chill at least one hour.

Roll to 1/8 inch thickness on pastry cloth sprinkled with flour. Lightly dip cookie cutters in flour before cutting. Bake at 400°F for 6 to 8 minutes. Makes 4 dozen 3-inch cookies.

Quick Maple Upside-Down Cake

Published with permission of Vermont Only:
www.vtonly.com/recipes.htm

"Topping"

- 1/3 c. butter
- 3/4 c. maple syrup
- 1/2 c. almond or cashew halves (if tolerated)

In a 9 by 9 inch pan melt 1/3 cup butter; add 3/4 cup maple syrup. Remove from heat and add 1/2 cup almond or cashew halves. Set aside.

"Batter"

In a mixing bowl combine:

- 1-1/3 c. all-purpose flour
- 2 t. baking powder
- 1/2 t. salt
- 1 c. white sugar

Add:

- 1/3 c. softened butter
- 2/3 c. milk
- 1 egg
- 1 t. vanilla

Mix well and beat until well blended. Pour batter over nuts and syrup and bake in preheated 350°F oven for 45 minutes, or until top springs back when touched lightly in center. Invert immediately onto serving plate and let stand 5 minutes. Cut into squares and serve warm, with whipped cream if desired.

Yellow Delicate Cake

Reprinted with permission Alicia's Recipes: www.aliciasrecipes.com

Ingredients

- 1-1/4 c. sugar
- 1/2 c. butter
- 2/3 c. milk
- 2 c. pastry flour
- 2 t. baking powder
- 1 t. vanilla
- 1/4 t. salt
- 3 eggs

Preheat over to 375°F. Grease and flour a 9 x 13 inch cake pan. Cream butter and sugar. Add milk, then flour sifted with the baking powder and salt. Add vanilla. Add eggs (unbeaten) one at a time and beat each one thoroughly into the mixture. Bake for 45 minutes. Top with Buttercream Frosting.

Buttercream Frosting

Ingredients

- 1-1/2 c. shortening
- 1/2 c. butter
- 1 t. vanilla
- 3 T. water
- 1 lb. or 4 c. powdered sugar

Using electric mixer on low, combine all ingredients in large mixing bowl. Beat on high for one minute only.

Butterscotch Brownies

Special thanks to Molly

Ingredients

- 1/4 c. shortening or butter
- 1 c. light brown sugar, packed
- 1 egg
- 1/2 t. vanilla
- 3/4 c. sifted flour
- 1 t. baking powder
- 1/2 t. salt
- 3/4 c. butterscotch chips

Heat oven to 350°F. Melt butter over low heat. Remove from heat and blend in brown sugar. Cool. Stir in egg and vanilla. In a separate bowl, sift together flour, baking powder. and salt. Stir dry mixture into butter, sugar, egg mixture. Fold in butterscotch chips. Spread in well-greased and floured square pan, 8 x 8 x 2 inches. Bake 20-25 minutes until a light touch with finger leaves a slight print. Cut into bars while warm. This is an old recipe and very good!

Caramelscotch Frosting

Adapted from *Amish-Country Cookbook, Vol. 1*

Ingredients

- 1 c. brown sugar, packed
- 3 T. shortening
- 2 T. butter
- 1/4 t. salt
- 1/3 c. milk
- 1-1/2 c. powdered sugar, sifted

Put brown sugar, shortening, butter, and salt in sauce pan. Cook over medium heat until mixture begins to bubble. Stir constantly. Add milk, mix well. Continue cooking over medium heat until mixture boils, stirring constantly. Boil vigorously 1 full minute.

Remove from heat and cool to lukewarm. Add powdered sugar all at once and beat until creamy and thick enough to spread. If it becomes too thick, soften over hot water. Will cover an 8-inch round double layer cake or a 9" x 13" single layer cake.

Kellogg's® Rice Krispies® Treats
Published with permission of The Kellogg Company

Ingredients
- 6 c. Kellogg's Rice Krispies cereal
- 3 T. margarine or butter
- 1 package (10 ounce, about 40) regular marshmallows or 4 cups miniature marshmallows.

Melt margarine in large saucepan over low heat. Add marshmallows and stir until completely melted. Remove from heat. Add Kelloggs® Rice Krispies® cereal. Stir until well-coated.

Using buttered spatula or waxed paper, press mixture evenly into 13 x 9 x 2 inch pan coated with cooking spray. Cut into 2-inch squares when cool. Best if served the same day.

Microwave Directions: Microwave margarine and marshmallows at HIGH two minutes in microwave-safe bowl. Stir to combine. Microwave at HIGH one minute longer. Stir until smooth. Add cereal. Stir until well coated. Press into pan as directed above. (Microwave cooking times may vary.)

Note: For best results, use fresh marshmallows. One jar (7 oz.) marshmallow crème can be substituted for marshmallows. Diet, reduced-calorie, or tub margarine is not recommended. Store no more than two days in airtight container.

Carrot Cake

Ingredients
- 2 c. sugar
- 1-1/2 c. canola oil
- 4 eggs
- 1 t. vanilla
- 2 c. sifted flour
- 1 t. cinnamon
- 2 t. baking soda
- 1/2 t. salt
- 3 c. finely grated carrots
- 1/2 c. chopped almonds, optional, if tolerated

Heat oven to 350°F. Grease and flour 9 x 13 inch cake pan.

Cream together sugar and oil. Add eggs and vanilla; beat until well mixed. Mix in flour, which has been sifted with cinnamon, salt, and soda. Slowly mix in carrots and nuts. Pour into greased and floured pan. Bake in pre-heated oven for 40 to 45 minutes or until toothpick inserted in center comes out clean. When cool, frost with Cream Cheese Frosting.

Cream Cheese Frosting

Ingredients
- 1/2 c. butter, softened
- 8 oz. cream cheese, softened
- 4 c. powdered sugar
- 1 t. vanilla extract

In a medium bowl, combine butter, cream cheese, powdered sugar, and vanilla. Beat until the mixture is smooth and creamy.

Grandma's Angel Food Cake

Ingredients
- 10 to 12 egg whites to equal 1-1/2 c.
- 1-1/4 c. powdered sugar
- 1 c. cake flour
- 1-1/2 t. cream of tartar
- 1-1/2 t. vanilla
- 1/4 t. salt
- 1 c. granulated sugar

Preparation: Move oven rack to lowest level. Heat oven to 350°F. After separating eggs, let rest at room temperature for 30 minutes. In second bowl, combine powdered sugar and flour. Sift mixture three or four times.

In large mixing bowl, add cream of tartar, vanilla, and salt to egg whites; beat on high speed. Add granulated sugar, beating until sugar is dissolved and stiff peaks form. Add dry ingredients into egg mixture 1/4 cup at a time, folding in by hand after each addition.

Gently spoon batter into an ungreased 10-inch angel food cake pan. Cut through batter with a knife to break up air bubbles. Bake at 350°F for 40-45 minutes or until cake springs back to the touch. Invert pan to cool to prevent collapse of cake. (If pan doesn't have its own stand, balance pan on a glass bottle.) Cool for at least an hour. Turn cake over; use a large serrated knife to loosen sides of the cake. Invert again over large plate or serving tray. Serve with whipped cream and blueberries.

Homemade Whipped Cream

Chill large mixing bowl and beaters before beginning. Beat 1 c. heavy cream on medium to form soft peaks. Add 1 t. vanilla and 1 T. powdered sugar and beat until stiff peaks form. Don't overbeat.

White Chocolate Bread Pudding
Recipe courtesy MealsForYou: www.mealsforyou.com

Ingredients
- 2 c. whole milk
- 1 c. granulated sugar
- 1-3/4 qt. heavy cream
- 1-1/4 lbs. white chocolate, chopped
- 4 eggs
- 15 egg yolks
- 1 loaf day-old French bread, cut into 1-inch slices
- aluminum foil

Preheat oven to 350°F. Heat milk, sugar, and all but 1/2 cup cream in a heavy saucepan over medium heat until the mixture just begins to bubble around the edges. Do not boil. Remove from heat. Stir in 10 ounces white chocolate until melted. Let **cool** 10 minutes. Lightly beat whole eggs and egg yolks in a bowl. Beat cream mixture into eggs in a slow and steady stream.

Arrange half the bread slices in a 9 x 13 inch baking dish. Pour half the egg mixture over bread. Press bread with the back of a spoon until soggy. Pour in remaining egg mixture. Cover pan with foil and **bake** 1 hour. Remove foil and **bake** another 30 minutes, until pudding is set and golden. Meanwhile, bring remaining cream just to a boil in a heavy saucepan. Remove from heat and stir in remaining white chocolate until completely melted. Serve over bread pudding.

Butterscotch Pie

Ingredients

- 2 T. butter
- 1 c. brown sugar
- 2/3 c. hot water
- 2 T. flour
- 3 T. cornstarch
- 1/2 t. salt
- 2 egg yolks
- 2 c. milk
- 1 t. vanilla
- 9-inch baked pie shell

Brown the butter in a heavy saucepan over medium heat; add the brown sugar and stir it until melted. Add the hot water and cook, stirring syrup until there are no lumps.

Mix together flour, cornstarch, salt, egg yolks and milk; slowly stir this mixture into the hot syrup. Boil everything until it thickens; then add the vanilla. Pour mixture into a baked pie shell and cool. Serve garnished with whipped cream and butterscotch chips.

Sherry's Rock Candy

Ingredients
- 3-3/4 c. sugar
- 1-1/2 c. white Karo® syrup
- 1 c. water
- 1 t. organic peppermint flavored oil, if tolerated
- 5 to 6 drops of organic food coloring

Lightly sprinkle cookie sheet with confectioner's sugar. Heat white sugar, water, and Karo® syrup over medium heat, mixing only until sugar dissolves. Do not keep stirring. Add flavoring and color.

Pour over powdered sugar in the cookie sheet. Cool until hardened. Break into smaller pieces.

Notes: Do not hover over pot while stirring or you could burn your eyes. Fill dirty sauce pan with water and boil immediately to simplify cleaning.

White Chocolate Almond Mounds

Ingredients
- 8 oz. white chocolate, broken in small pieces
- 1 c. toasted, unsalted almonds

Place chocolate in medium glass or other microwave-safe bowl. Microwave on 30% power for 15 seconds. Stir chocolate and return to microwave for 5 seconds. Stir again. Repeat in 5 second intervals until melted. Stir in almonds. Drop by heaping tablespoons onto waxed paper. Refrigerate until cool and hardened. Store in airtight container in refrigerator.

White Chocolate Fudge

Ingredients
- 1 8-oz. pkg. of cream cheese, softened
- 4 c. powdered sugar
- 1-1/2 t. vanilla
- 12 oz. white chocolate, chopped up
- 3/4 c. chopped almonds, if tolerated

Grease an 8 x 8 inch baking dish. In a medium bowl, beat cream cheese, sugar, and vanilla until smooth. Heat white chocolate in the top of a double boiler over lightly simmering water, stirring until smooth. Fold melted white chocolate and almonds into cream cheese mixture. Spread into prepared baking dish. Chill for 1 hour. Cut into 1-inch squares

Maple Sugar Candy

Ingredients
- 2 c. maple syrup
- 3/4 c. milk
- 2 T. butter
- 48 mini marshmallows
- 1/2 c. chopped almonds, if tolerated

Boil together syrup, milk. and butter to soft ball stage (240°F). Let cool a few minutes; then beat until creamy.

Spread marshmallows and nuts on a greased sheet. Pour maple cream over nuts and marshmallows and spread out on sheet.

Homemade Marshmallows

I couldn't resist publishing this recipe courtesy of Linda Stradley of *What's Cooking America*: www.whatscookingamerica.net. How much more fun can you have than making your own marshmallows?

Ingredients

- Powdered sugar
- 3-1/2 envelopes (2 tablespoons plus 2-1/2 teaspoons) unflavored gelatin
- 1/2 c. cold water
- 2 c. sugar
- 1/2 c. light corn syrup
- 1/2 c. hot water
- 1/4 t. salt
- 3 egg whites, room temperature
- 2 t. vanilla extract

Line the bottom and sides of a 13 x 9 inch baking pan with plastic wrap; oil and then generously dust bottom and sides with powdered sugar.

In large bowl of an electric mixer, sprinkle gelatin over the 1/2 cup cold water; let stand to soften.

In a large, heavy saucepan, cook sugar, corn syrup, hot water, and salt over low heat, stirring until sugar is dissolved. Increase heat to medium-high and boil mixture approximately 4 to 5 minutes, without stirring, until a candy or digital thermometer registers 240°F or syrup reaches the firm-ball stage (when a small amount of syrup is dropped into very cold water, it forms a ball that holds its shape when pressed); immediately remove from heat.

Pour hot sugar mixture over gelatin mixture, stirring until gelatin is dissolved. Beat mixture on high speed approximately 5 to 6 minutes or until white, thick, and nearly tripled in volume.

In another large bowl with clean beaters, beat whites until they just hold stiff peaks; beat egg whites and vanilla into sugar mixture until well combined. Pour mixture into prepared baking pan; sift 1/4 cup powdered sugar evenly over top. Refrigerate marshmallow, uncovered, until firm (at least 3 hours).

Run a thin knife around edges of pan and invert pan onto a large cutting board; remove plastic wrap. Sprinkle top with 1/4 cup powdered sugar. Lightly grease the blade of a large knife, trim edges of marshmallow. Pressing down firmly with the full length of the blade, cut the marshmallow into 1-inch cubes. NOTE: To cut into even 1-inch squares, use a ruler and toothpicks to mark it every 1 inch. Sift additional powdered sugar over the tops if necessary. Store either covered with plastic wrap, in the refrigerator, or in an airtight container. Makes about 80 candies.

Variation for Peppermint Marshmallows: Add 3/4 teaspoon peppermint extract instead of the vanilla extract. After pouring the marshmallow mixture into the pan, quickly drop dots of red food coloring across the surface of the marshmallow. Use a toothpick to swirl the food coloring into the marshmallows to create a marbleized effect. Dust with confectioner's sugar.

.

Beverages

Beverages

One of the great debates among nutrition scientists is how much water a person should drink. The debate gets even more complex when you talk about interstitial cystitis (IC) and overactive bladder (OAB). Obviously, a person that drinks constantly during the day will also be running to the bathroom. But for people whose symptoms are affected by the type of food that they eat, water can help dilute the effects of the bad foods with the potential to reduce symptoms. Probably the best advice that I can give you is to listen to your body. If you are thirsty, have something to drink. In fact, many people with bladder problems find they do better if they sip on water all day long rather than drink large glasses at a time. What kind of water should you drink? IC patients may have to experiment. In general, filtered tap water is fine. You might also try distilled water or other types of bottled water.

The other question that comes up frequently is about coffee and tea. IC and OAB patients should all avoid anything with caffeine. Trust me, it makes a difference. If you are having trouble getting off of your daily caffeine, start slowly by alternating your caffeinated beverage with water. After a few days, have two glasses of water between each caffeinated beverage. Eventually, you will be able to avoid caffeine entirely.

If you are looking for coffee and tea substitutes, check out the Interstitial Cystitis Network Shop: www.icnshop.com. They have a wonderful selection of coffee substitutes and teas. In addition, you can find chamomile, peppermint, and blueberry tea at most grocery stores. Just be sure to read the labels. Some herbal teas, even if they are labeled caffeine-free, may also contain black or green teas. Naturally, you want to avoid those.

Other options for drinks include dairy products, almond milk, pear juice, blueberry juice, and even low-acid orange juice. Again, listen to your body. If you seem to have an increase in symptoms, put the offending beverage on your list to try again at a later date. Many bladder patients find that, over time, they can add more variety to their limited selection of beverages.

Vanilla Horchata

Adapted with permission of The Vanilla.COMpany (www.vanilla.com)

Ingredients

- 1 can evaporated milk (may substitute almond or rice milk)
- 2 vanilla beans, split (or 2 T. pure vanilla extract), preferably Mexican
- 1-1/2 cups medium- or long-grain white rice, cooked soft
- 3-1/2 cups water (or more, to taste)
- 1 c. sugar (or more to taste)
- Ground nutmeg or cinnamon to dust over served horchata (optional)

Heat milk with the vanilla beans in a medium saucepan. Allow to cool. Combine rice, water, and sugar in a blender, and blend on high speed for several minutes, until the mixture is very smooth. (You may need to do this in a few batches.)

Strain rice mixture into a pitcher using a fine sieve (use cheese cloth if you don't have a good sieve). Add milk with the vanilla beans removed; then scrape some of the vanilla seeds into the Horchata. (Rinse the beans well and dry them for using a second time.) If using extract, add now. Taste, and adjust sweetness to taste.

Refrigerate until ready to serve. Serve plain or over ice. Use a vanilla bean as a swizzle stick and dust with nutmeg or cinnamon if desired.

Hot Vanilla Milk

Ingredients
- 2 c. milk
- ½ t. vanilla
- 2 t. powdered sugar

Combine ingredients in saucepan. Heat on low to medium heat, stirring constantly. Top with whipped cream if desired.

White Hot Chocolate

Ingredients
- 2 c. milk
- 3/4 c. white chocolate chips
- Whipped topping

Heat 1/2 cup milk and chips over medium heat, whisking until chocolate melts. Stir in remaining milk and heat to warm. Garnish with whipped cream. Serves 2.

Variations:

Hot White Chocolate Peppermint Milk: Melt crushed peppermint candy into the white chocolate chip mixture.

Hot Butterscotch Milk: Substitute butterscotch chips for white chocolate chips.

Hot Carob Milk: Substitute carob chips for white chocolate chips. Add dash of vanilla.

Hot Spiced Pear Juice

Ingredients
- 4 c. pear juice
- 3 sticks of cinnamon
- 4 cloves
- 1/4 t. nutmeg
- 4 T. honey

Here is a great use for that coffee maker you cannot use anymore. Set up coffee maker with coffee filter in basket. Measure spices into filter. Pour juice in the machine where you would normally put water and let run. (Check the instructions of your coffee maker to be sure this is okay for your machine.) Sweeten with honey.

White Chocolate Milkshake

Ingredients
- 1/2 c. vanilla ice cream
- 1/2 c. skim milk
- 4 to 5 ice cubes
- Dash of vanilla extract
- 2 T. white chocolate sauce (I like Torani)

"Buzz" all of the ingredients in a blender, and within minutes, you have a wonderful treat! Serves 1.

Note: Those who like to add protein to their shakes or smoothies should avoid soy powders and opt for 100% pure whey powder, since soy is often a trigger food for IC patients.

Vanilla Malt Shake

Ingredients
- 1 c. all-natural vanilla bean ice cream
- 1-1/2 c. milk
- 1/2 t. vanilla
- 2 T. malt powder

"Buzz" all of the ingredients in a blender. High in protein and antioxidants. Serves 2.

Blueberry Smoothie

Ingredients
- 1 c. blueberries
- 1 c. plain or vanilla yogurt (if tolerated, otherwise add additional 1 c. milk)
- 1 c. milk
- 1 t. sugar
- 6 ice cubes
- 2 T. whey protein

"Buzz" all of the ingredients in a blender. High in protein and antioxidants. Serves 2.

Vanilla Pear Smoothie

Ingredients
- 1 16-oz. can pears with natural juice
- 2 c. milk
- 1 t. vanilla
- 1 t. sugar
- 6 ice cubes
- 2 T. whey protein

"Buzz" all of the ingredients in a blender. High in protein and antioxidants. Serves 4.

Appendices

Appendix A: Discovering Your Personal Trigger Foods

If you have been diagnosed with interstitial cystitis (IC) or overactive bladder (OAB), dietary modification is entirely within your control and can be one of the most successful ways to manage your symptoms.

You probably already suspect that certain foods trigger your symptoms. For most IC and OAB patients, the worst offenders are tomato products, cranberry juice, citrus fruits, soy, coffee, tea, sodas, alcoholic beverages, and chocolate. Patients with OAB may find they have fewer trigger foods than a person with IC.

What Is an "Elimination Diet"?

An "elimination diet" is just a fancy way to organize the testing of various foods that may be contributing to your symptoms. In order to get a clear picture of which foods affect your bladder symptoms, you need to keep good records. You might be familiar with diaries used to record your symptoms, and others where you record your food intake. Tools to help you are included in this Appendix:

    i.   IC Food List
    ii. Sample Pain Scale
    iii. Symptoms Diary
    iv. Food Intake Diary

Feel free to copy them as needed or use them as a model to create charts in your personal journal. You can also download these documents at www.nutraconsults.com/CCresources.html.

When examining the IC Food List, notice that the left hand column is labeled "Usually OK," the middle column is labeled "May Be OK," and the right hand column is labeled "Usually Problematic." These designations are based on years of reports from veteran IC patients and physicians. OAB patients often report similar responses to foods; however no matter what the cause, individuals with fussy bladders will respond differently to different foods. Therefore, the list is not meant to be a good food/bad food list; rather it should be used as a guideline for determining your personal trigger foods. Some important things to remember when using the list:

- Most patients are able to eat a few of the foods listed as "problematic."
- Occasionally patients must avoid some foods listed as "Usually OK."
- Food may have different effects on people in raw and cooked forms.
- Patients may experience different symptoms from food at various stages of the disease.
- Reading ingredient labels of pre-packaged foods is critical to help avoid preservatives and artificial sweeteners, flavors, and coloring.
- Most patients need to avoid flavor enhancers such as monosodium glutamate (MSG)—other ingredients that signal MSG in a product are: hydrolyzed vegetable protein (HVP), hydrolyzed plant protein (HPP), natural flavoring (may have HVP), Accent, Zest, and Chinese seasoning.
- After treatment, many IC patients find that they can add back some foods in small quantities.

Preparing to Experiment

Maintaining a positive attitude during this process is incredibly important. This is not an exercise in deprivation; it is an exercise in healing! When you take the challenge to determine your personal trigger foods, you take control of your health and empower yourself to live as normal a life as possible.

There are three phases to this IC/OAB elimination diet strategy. Trying to figure out your trigger foods can be a mental and organizational challenge. When you have a fussy bladder, you may not have the time and energy to try new recipes and plan bladder-friendly meals. Because of that, I encourage you to do the first two phases of the system during a time when your calendar is relatively clear.

- **Week One (Baseline):** Record your normal food intake, pain levels, and voiding habits.
- **Weeks Two and Three (Minimal Diet):** Consume a minimal diet based on foods from the "Usually OK" column.
- **Testing Period:** Methodically test foods one at a time for three days before testing the next new food.

Week One (Baseline Diet)

It is important to know which foods you are eating and what your baseline bladder symptoms are before you start your elimination diet. To find out your baseline, write down everything you eat and record your bladder symptoms for one week using the diaries provided. Keep good notes, especially on pain levels, food preparation methods, and other activities that may affect your symptoms. To standardize how you record your level of pain, you can use the *Sample Pain Scale* included in this appendix. It isn't necessary to determine cause and effect just yet. This is just a snapshot of what is happening before you make any dietary changes.

Weeks Two and Three (Minimal Diet)

To avoid feeling deprived, it is important to eat foods that you are familiar with, especially in the beginning. Take a look at the *Sample Grocery List* (Appendix C, pg. 169) that was created from the *IC Food List*. Start personalizing your grocery list by circling the foods that you like and avoiding the foods that you already suspect give you problems. You might want to make separate copies of the list for your refrigerator to have handy at work and to keep in your purse or wallet. Although the list may seem limited at first, in just a few weeks you will be adding many more foods to your personal "Usually OK" list.

Over the next two weeks, only choose foods from your personalized "Usually OK" list. If you get stuck, review Chapter 1 for hints on meal planning. A meal plan created from the "Usually OK" food list is not nutrient deficient. Also, please remember to keep detailed *Voiding and Pain Diaries* and *Food Intake Diaries* during this time.

Hint: To simplify the recording of your food intake, use your Food Intake Diaries as planning sheets. Each evening, take some time to write down what you "plan" to eat the next day. Then, all you have to do is record the time that you ate each meal. If you do not eat what you originally planned, just change what you wrote the night before.

Hopefully, after completing these two weeks, you will experience some relief from your IC pain and frequency. If you don't think you have reduced your symptoms significantly, compare your pain diaries from the first week to the third week. You might not take your symptoms down to "0" or feel completely normal, but a two or three level reduction in your level of pain and/or reducing the number of times you void should be considered significant improvement.

If after you compare your diaries to previous weeks, you still do not feel you have improved significantly, you may want to consider one of these options:

- Follow the "Usually OK" diet for another week and reassess your results.
- Get some help deciphering your diaries from your physician or a registered dietitian.
- Try eating a more restrictive diet, but only under the guidance of a registered dietitian or your physician.

Testing Period

After two weeks of limiting your food choices, you will be eager to try something new. To stay organized, I recommend that you create a list of foods that you would like to try. Choose from foods that you miss the most, foods that are on the "Maybe OK" list, foods that add flavor, and foods that will improve your total nutritional intake. Examples of what you might try include:

- Blueberries
- Blackberries
- Bananas
- Onions
- Low-acid juices
- Whole wheat bread
- Almonds
- Spinach
- Yogurt
- Black Pepper

Since testing some foods might increase your symptoms temporarily, it is a good idea to choose a couple of days when you can observe your symptoms and then take it easy if your bladder flares. Usually a three-day trial is long enough to determine if a food is going to affect you or not. The steps for testing new foods are:

1. Test one food at a time.
2. Try a small portion of the food the first day.
3. If you don't experience any increase in symptoms, try a larger portion the next day.
4. If you are still doing fine, try to eat a couple of portions of the food on the third day.
5. If you do not react, you can add that food to your personal "Usually OK" grocery list!

If you react to a food at any time, simply record the reaction and note to try the food again later. Sometimes other things are happening in your life that can cause your symptoms to flare, and when you try the food later, you will find that your bladder is not affected. Also, if your bladder becomes fussy when trying a food, wait a day or so for your symptoms to subside before trying the next food on your list. If you are an IC patient, you might ask your physician about using a urinary anesthetic like Pyridium to calm your bladder if you flare from a food. Mixing a half teaspoon of baking soda into a glass of water and drinking it can also temporarily quiet down your bladder. (Using baking soda on a daily basis often backfires, so use this trick on an infrequent basis only.)

Repeating this testing process with each food on your list may seem like a long and tedious process, but by systematically adding foods, staying organized, and carefully recording your symptoms, you will be more confident of your food choices.

Finally, a common question asked by patients is, "How long from the mouth to the bladder?" Unfortunately, the answer is vague, depending on the person and the food. Some foods, like cranberry juice, will likely cause a reaction in an IC patient within an hour. Other foods might not cause a reaction in small doses, but you could react when you increase the portion size. Some patients will experience an increase in symptoms right before bedtime and others report a day or two lag between eating a food and the development of symptoms. In most cases, however, if you are going to experience symptoms with a particular food, it will most likely happen within hours.

i. The IC Food List

Note: Foods labeled with a plus sign (+) can be especially soothing during an IC flare.

Beverages

Bladder Friendly	Try It	Caution
water – *try different kinds* juice – *blueberry, pear* milk+ milk substitutes – *almond+, rice, Lactaid+* milkshake – *vanilla+* tea – *chamomile+, peppermint+* non-dairy creamers – *check label* eggnog – *non alcoholic+, without problem ingredients*	juice – *low-acid orange, grape, some apple, baby* coffee & coffee substitutes - *herbal, low-acid decaf, roasted carob* tea – *alfalfa, roasted carob* soda – *root beer with ice (decaffeinated, not diet)* sports drinks – *test to find one that works for you (e.g., blue Gatorade)*	alcohol – *irritating and often contraindicated with many IC medications* water – *carbonated, vitamin, flavored* juice – *cranberry, orange, acai* milk – *chocolate, soy* coffee – *regular, decaf* teas – *regular, green, herbal* sodas – *colas, citrus, diet* drink powders – *Kool-aid®, or powdered ice tea drinks* sports drinks energy drinks – *guarana, mate*

Dairy

Bladder Friendly	Try It	Caution
cheeses – *American, mozzarella, cheddar cheese (mild), feta, ricotta+, string cheeses+* cream cheese cottage cheese+ ice cream+ – *most* milk+ milk substitutes – *Lactaid* sherbet – *no citrus or chocolate flavors* Rice Dream® dessert – *vanilla* whipped cream – *from dairy, Cool Whip, Dream Whip*	cheeses – *blue cheese, brie, brick parmesan, camembert, cheddar cheese (sharp), edam, emmenthaler, gruyere hard jack, Monterey Jack, parmesan (fresh & canned), Roquefort, stilton, Swiss* buttermilk sour cream –*accent on a baked potato or soup* pizza –*plain, chicken & garlic, veggie or made with white sauce - no pepperoni* sorbet yogurt –*blueberry, vanilla, plain*	cheeses – *processed, Cheez Whiz* ice cream – *caution with citrus or chocolate flavors* soy products – *soy milk, soy cheeses*

Meats, Fish, Poultry, and Protein

Bladder Friendly	Try It	Caution
eggs+ poultry – *chicken+, turkey* fish+ beef+ seafood – *clams, crabmeat (not canned), lobster, shrimp* lamb+ pork protein powder – *whey, egg whites* veal liver – *beef or chicken*	garden/veggie burgers – *without soy products* beef – *corned beef* sandwich meats – *liverwurst, ham (fresh or boiled, without heavy preservatives or flavorings.)* bacon anchovies caviar prosciutto sausages – *without problem ingredients*	cured meats – *bologna, pepperoni, salami* canned crab meat hot dogs sausage – *most* smoked fish soy products – *soy veggie patties, protein powder, tofu*

Vegetables

Bladder Friendly	Try It	Caution
asparagus avocado beans – *black eyed peas, garbanzo, lentils, pinto, white, most dried beans* beets broccoli brussels sprouts cabbage carrots⁺ cauliflower celery chives corn⁺ cucumber eggplant green beans greens – *collard greens, kale, mustard greens, okra, swiss chard, spinach, bok choy* lettuce & most salad greens mushrooms⁺ olives – *black* parsley⁺ peas – *green⁺, snow peas, split peas* bell peppers – *yellow, orange, red* potatoes⁺– *white, yams* pumpkin radishes rhubarb rutabaga squash⁺ – *most, plus zucchini* turnips	beans – *fava, kidney beans, lima beans, black beans* bell peppers – *green* olives – *green* greens – *chicory, dandelion greens, purslane, turnip greens* leeks (cooked) onions – *white, red, cooked bulb onion, raw green* tomatoes – *homegrown, low acid* watercress	chili peppers onions – *raw bulb onions* pickles sauerkraut soy beans – *edamame, roasted* tomato – *tomato sauces, tomato juice* tofu

Fruits

Bladder Friendly	Try It	Caution
apples – *Gala, Fuji, Pink Lady* applesauce – *homemade with Gala, Fuji or Pink Lady apples* blueberries⁺ coconut – *without preservatives* dates – *without preservatives* pears⁺ rhubarb watermelon	applesauce – *canned or baby* apricots bananas berries – *blackberries, raspberries, olallieberries* cherimoya cherries – *fresh, maraschino* citrus peels currants figs mango melon – *Crenshaw, honeydew* peaches plums raisins – *brown*	berries – *cranberries, most* citrus dried fruit – *with preservatives* grapes guava kiwi fruit melons – *cantaloupe* nectarines passion fruit papaya persimmon pineapple starfruit strawberries raisins – *golden*

Grains

Bladder Friendly	Try It	Caution
breads – *corn bread+, oat bread+, pita, potato bread+, white bread+, Italian sweet bread, whole wheat bread (i.e. Ezekiel)* **cereals** – *most cereals without problem ingredients, oat cereal, rice cereal (hot or cold)* **crackers** – *matzo* **grains** – *couscous, grits, millet, quinoa+, spelt* **flours** – *buckwheat, wheat* **pasta** **rice+**	**breads** – *rye, sourdough* **cereals** – *instant packaged hot cereal* **crackers** – *without problem ingredients* **grain** – *amaranth*	**breads** – *made with unsafe ingredients and/or heavily processed and fortified* **cereals** – *heavily preserved, sweetened, heavily fortified, flavored,* **flour** – *soy* **pasta** – *prepared or boxed pasta dishes* **rice** – *boxed dishes*

Soups

Bladder Friendly	Try It	Caution
homemade soup & stock – *from okay meats and vegetables*	**soups** – *canned, low sodium, organic soups (without problem ingredients)*	**bouillon** – *cubes, powder* **canned**– *most* **packaged soups** – *most*

Sweets and Desserts

Bladder Friendly	Try It	Caution
berries – *blueberries* **cake** – *homemade pound cake*, angel food*,* homemade white/yellow cakes*, carrot* **frostings** – *homemade vanilla frosting, homemade caramel frosting, carob, whipped cream* **carob** **cookies** – *oatmeal*, shortbread, sugar* **muffins** – *carrot* **cheesecake** **crème brûlée** **custards+** **pie** – *custard, cream pie, homemade apple pie (with safe apples), pumpkin pie* **divinity** **sweet breads** – *homemade zucchini bread+* **maple syrup** **pastries** – *plain, almond, pear* **ice cream** – *peppermint, vanilla+* **pudding** – *tapioca, vanilla+, rice+* **milkshake** – *vanilla*+* **sweeteners** – *brown sugar, honey*, sugar*	**artificial sweeteners** – *Splenda® (sucralose)* **candy** – *caramel, licorice* **chocolate** – *white* **ice cream** – *caramel, coconut, mango, peppermint, butter pecan* **sorbet** – *coconut* **pastries** – *blueberry, cinnamon* **popsicles** – *some* **sweet bread** – *banana* **yogurt** – *frozen*	**artificial sweeteners** – *acesulfame K aspartame, NutraSweet®, saccharine, Sweet-N-Low, stevia* **candy** – *red hot-type cinnamon* **chocolate** – *cocoa, milk, bittersweet, dark* **ice cream** – *chocolate, coffee, rocky road* **sorbets** – *with problem fruits* **pastries** – *with problem fruits* **pie** – *pecan, mincemeat* **desserts** – *with problem nuts* **fruitcakes**

Snacks

Bladder Friendly	Try It	Caution
almonds carrots celery chips (plain) – *corn , potato* crackers – *soda or soup* fruit bars – *blueberry, pear* milkshake – *vanilla* oatmeal bars peanuts, peanut butter popcorn pretzels – *plain*	donuts – *glazed, old fashioned* graham crackers fruit & nut bars – *with safe ingredients* licorice pizza – *plain, chicken & garlic, veggie or made with white sauce - no pepperoni*	chips – *potato (seasoned, barbequed)* dessert cakes – *fast food restaurants*

Fats, Oils, Nuts, and Seeds

Bladder Friendly	Try It	Caution
nuts – *almonds, cashews, peanuts* butters – *almond, peanut* oils – *canola, coconut, corn, olive, peanut, safflower, sesame, soy* margarine lard shortening salad dressing – *homemade without problem ingredients*	nuts – *macadamia, pecans, walnuts* mayonnaise tahini seeds – *sunflower seeds* shortening – *butter-flavored*	nuts – *filberts, hazelnuts, pecans, pistachios* oils – *check label* salad dressings – *most*

Condiments, Seasonings, and Additives

Bladder Friendly	Try It	Caution
allspice almond extract anise basil⁺ caraway seed coriander dill fennel garlic⁺ mace marjoram⁺ oregano⁺ poppy seed rosemary⁺ sage⁺ salt – *in small quantities* thyme tarragon vanilla extract	black pepper celery seed cilantro cinnamon – *powdered* citric acid – *in small quantities* cumin – *in small quantities* dried parsley dried chervil ginger lemon extract mayonnaise malt powder nutmeg onion powder orange extract turmeric	ascorbic acid autolyzed yeast BHA and BHT benzoates catsup (ketchup) cayenne cloves chili powder horseradish hot curry powder hydrolyzed protein meat tenderizers metabisulfites miso MSG – *monosodium glutamate* mustard oleoresin paprika paprika pickles red pepper soy sauce sulfites tamari vinegar Worcestershire sauce

ii. Sample Pain Scale

Level 1: I feel no symptoms of IC. I can do anything.

Level 2: I feel slight discomfort, possibly the beginning of a flare. I can do anything.

Level 3: I feel mild symptoms of IC. It is not stopping me from my daily life, but I am feeling some mild discomfort.

Level 4: I feel moderate symptoms of IC and have a moderate need to urinate, with a moderate level of pain. My activities are limited. My frequency is higher, and I am looking for restrooms and using them. At this point, I am on my way home to rest and begin my pain management strategies and/or medication.

Level 5: I am very uncomfortable, perhaps biting my lip and/or holding my abdomen. I am usually lying in bed now. Walking is more painful now. IC has limited me from doing my daily functions. I am utilizing some of my pain management medications and tools at this point.

Level 6: I am having constant intense pelvic pain with moderate frequency and urgency. I am worried and ready to call my doctor for advice.

Level 7: I am in bed in severe pain. I am using all of my coping strategies, but I may need help at this point. I am considering calling my doctor and may go to the emergency room for help.

Level 8: I am having difficulty tolerating the pain. I am calling my doctor.

Level 9: Pain is intolerable; I am on my way to the emergency room because I need help in managing my pain.

Level 10: Excruciating pain

Reprinted with permission from Interstitial Cystitis Network

iii. Voiding and Pain Diary				
Date	Time	Volume	Pain Level (1-10)	Notes

iv. Food Intake Diary				
Date	Time	Food	Amount	Preparation

Appendix B: Food for an IC Flare

What Is a Flare?

An interstitial cystitis (IC) flare is the intense return of IC symptoms in a patient who has been relatively pain free. Symptoms of a flare can include urinary frequency, urgency, and pain. Patients in a flare may also experience extreme fatigue, anxiety, and depression as they struggle to cope with the recurrence of symptoms they thought were under control.

Sometimes flares can dissipate in a day, or they may continue for months at a time. Many times an IC patient will believe that they have a urinary tract infection (UTI), only to find that their urine sample is sterile (I often say that people with IC are the only people who are happy when a urinalysis shows they have a UTI, because they can actually do something about it!).

Examples of things that can precipitate a flare are certain foods, sexual intercourse, constipation, diarrhea, restrictive clothing, pre-menstrual syndrome, heavy exercise, and unmanaged stress. Sometimes, however, there is no way to determine what caused a flare.

IC Rescue Diet

If certain foods can trigger your symptoms, it only makes sense that you should choose bladder-safe foods if you are in a flare. The very safest foods include plain chicken, pears, green beans, carrots, rice, distilled or filtered water, milk, eggs, and white bread products. Since flares are unpredictable, it is also wise to keep these foods on hand. Keep chicken, green beans, and white bread in the freezer to pull out at the last minute. Pears and carrots can be canned. Rice can be instant or long grain. (I love using a rice maker. In twenty minutes, we have the base for almost any meal!)

You should see positive results within three days of following this very minimal "rescue" diet. Please note that this diet can be nutritionally deficient and should not be consumed for longer than a week. Therefore, I recommend that you contact your physician if you do not experience relief after a few days. If your physician says that you need to follow this minimal diet longer than a week, a registered dietitian can help you choose foods to maximize your nutritional intake.

Sample Rescue Menus

When you are in a flare, you may not have the energy to create meal plans, so I have included some sample meal plans to get you started:

Breakfast:
Scrambled eggs and toast with butter
Pears
Milk

Lunch:
Chicken sandwich with white bread
Carrots
Pears
Milk

Choose a Snack:
Bagel, toast, hard-boiled egg, carrots, pears, milk

Dinner:
Chicken
Rice
Green beans
Pears
Milk

Other Self-Help Strategies

Although this book is focused specifically on diet, there are some other things you can do to minimize a flare. If you are constipated or have diarrhea, other dietary adjustments may be more appropriate than the rescue diet provided. Drinking more water and adding fiber are simple self-care ways to correct these problems. If intestinal problems persist, ask your physician for other treatment recommendations.

Other flare management techniques include getting plenty of rest, practicing stress reduction strategies, taking warm baths with Epsom salts or baking soda, writing in your journal, and talking to other IC or OAB patients. Heating pads can fool the body into thinking that you are not feeling any pelvic pain. (Hint: I like the portability and convenience of the microwavable and stick-on pads.) You might also talk to your doctor about medications you can use specifically for a flare.

You will be more comfortable if you wear loose clothing when you have a flare. Medical scrubs, pajama pants, and sweat pants with adjustable waistbands are good choices. Women may also be more comfortable in jumpers or loose sundresses. Flat shoes or slippers are easier on your back than shoes with heels.

Sometimes when you have a flare, it is hard to think past the pain. To simplify the coping process, you might want to create a list of things to do when you get a flare. Include your urologist's phone number, sample menus, and a list of medicines to take, and remind yourself to rest.

Finally, enlist the help of your loved ones. If you prefer not to talk about your illness all the time, decide on a secret phrase to use with your family and friends that signals that you have an angry bladder. Even small children can understand that your tummy hurts, and most will be content to cuddle on the couch with you and do quiet things.

Flare Coping References

Since finding ways to cope with flares often means trial and error, the best way to learn is either to talk to other IC patients at local support groups or ask questions in an online support group community like the Interstitial Cystitis Network (www.ic-network.com/forum).

You will probably want to read everything you can about flare management strategy. Please be careful when choosing books about IC or any other health problem. Avoid anything that promises a cure or suggests using any non-documented therapies. A good place to check for a book's credibility is on the websites for the Interstitial Cystitis Association (www.ichelp.org) or the Interstitial Cystitis Network (www.ic-network.com). If the book is not sold or recommended by those organizations, it is probably not worth your money.

When to Contact your Doctor

I often tell the story of when my husband and I drove from Michigan to Florida with our three children—about a twenty-hour drive. I was feeling worse than usual, but I assumed that it was my bladder flaring. Instead of calling the doctor, I took some pain medication, hoping that would relieve my symptoms. Unfortunately, I continued to go downhill, and I finally asked my husband to stop at an emergency room in north Florida. The doctor said I had the worst urinary tract infection he had ever seen! Thankfully, after 24 hours on antibiotics, I felt wonderful and was able to enjoy our vacation.

The lesson is, call your doctor immediately if you experience any of these "red flag" symptoms:

- Severe pain that is not controlled by your normal medications
- Pain or frequency that is *different* than your usual symptoms
- Fever or chills
- Difficulty urinating
- Blood in the urine
- Cloudy or foul-smelling urine

Recovering From a Flare

Regardless of which coping strategies you use to get your bladder under control, it is important not to overdo it when you feel better. It may be tempting to work overtime to catch up on chores and work, but I really believe it is important to rest and eat only the most bladder friendly foods for a week or so after you recover.

Also, try to think about what may have caused the flare in the first place and add these thoughts to your journal. Did you wear restrictive clothing or try a new food? Were you under more stress than usual, or were you not getting enough sleep? By scrutinizing the things that may have caused you to flare, you can minimize your chances for another one!

Appendix C: Grocery Store List	
Fresh Fruits	
Pears	Blueberries
Coconut (no preservatives)	Dates (no preservatives)
Fresh Vegetables	
Broccoli	Brussels sprouts
Fresh oregano	Cabbage
Fresh garlic	Carrots
Fresh basil	Baby carrots
Zucchini	Cauliflower
Yams	Chives
Sweet Potatoes	Greens
Turnips	Corn
Cucumber	Mushrooms
Okra	Lettuce and other salad greens
Parsley	Peas
Pumpkin	Squash
Radishes	Potatoes
	Snow peas

Canned Fruits/Juices	
Canned pears	Gerber® pear juice
Organic blueberry juice	Gerber baby food pears

Canned Vegetables	
Carrots	Corn
Kidney beans	Greens
Black beans	Green or yellow beans
Navy beans	Mushrooms
Peas	Yams
Sweet potatoes	Pumpkin

Frozen Goods	
Broccoli	Carrots
Vanilla ice cream	Corn
Blueberries	Peas
	Mixed vegetables

Oils, Fats, and Nuts	
Olive oil	Canola or other vegetable oil
Butter	Shortening (trans-fat free)
Margarine	Cooking spray

Dairy and Eggs	
Milk (preferably non-fat)	Evaporated skim milk
Cream cheese	Dried milk
String cheese	Feta cheese
Ricotta	Mozzarella cheese
	Whipping cream

Baking Products	
Flour	Sugar
Almond extract	Honey
Natural vanilla extract	Corn meal
Maple syrup	Muffin mix
Vanilla frosting	Baking soda
Vanilla pudding	Baking powder
Caramel	Carob powder
White chocolate chips	Carob chips
Butterscotch chips	Dried egg whites

Seasonings	
Allspice	Anise
Caraway seed	Basil
Tarragon	Poppy seed
Rosemary	Marjoram
Sage	Dill
Salt	Fennel
Thyme	Garlic salt or powder
Oregano	Mace
	Cinnamon (if tolerated)

Dried Goods	
Long grain rice	Instant rice
Elbow macaroni	Mashed potato flakes
Linguini	Dried beans, lentils, or peas
Angel hair pasta	Egg noodles
Pasta shells	Spaghetti

Breads/Snacks	
White bread	Oat bread
Vanilla wafers	Pita bread
All natural potato chips	English muffins
All natural pretzels	Bagels
Sugar candy in "safe" flavors	Blueberry muffins
Popcorn	Sugar cookies
All natural pita or bagel chips	Flour tortillas

Meats, Poultry, and Seafood	
Beef	Chicken
Shrimp	Fish
Lobster	Lamb
Scallops	Liver
Turkey	Pork
Veal	Crab

Miscellaneous	
Paper plates	Paper napkins
Paper bowls	Disposable utensils
Paper towels	Zipper bags for freezing
Aluminum foil	Reynolds's Cooking Bags®
Plastic wrap	Cheese cloth
Wax paper	Freezer paper

Appendix D: Great IC and OAB Resources

Organizations

Confident Choices
P.O. Box 210086
Auburn Hills, MI 48321
Web address: www.nutraconsults.com/confidentchoices.html
Email: NutraConsults@aol.com
Phone: 248-961-3613

Confident Choices, a nutrition education company, was
established to educate patients and medical professionals about
the unique nutritional and lifestyle needs of interstitial cystitis
patients.

Highlights of Confident Choices:
- Individual and group nutrition and lifestyle counseling
  exclusively for IC patients by a registered dietitian who
  specializes in IC
- Consultation—traditional office visits, home visits, and
  phone consultations
- Support group workshops about IC dietary modification,
  lifestyle strategies, and supplement education
- Continuing education workshops for registered dietitians
- A monthly newsletter dedicated to providing IC dietary
  support, resources, and reviews of research
- The IC Shop Online, interfacing with ICN's IC Shop and
  Amazon.com to provide purchasing options for IC food
  and comfort products as well as educational resources

Interstitial Cystitis Association (ICA)

Web Address: www.ichelp.org

E-mail: icamail@ichelp.org

Telephone: 301-610-5300

Toll-free: 800-HELP ICA

The ICA is committed to finding more effective treatments and a cure for interstitial cystitis. The authoritative source of IC information in the US, the ICA promotes and funds research; educates the medical community and public; advocates for IC patients, healthcare providers and researchers; and offers support for IC patients and their families.

The ICA is dedicated to helping all those living with IC, as well as the healthcare providers and researchers who strive to improve the lives of IC patients by providing:

- Pilot grant funding through the Fishbein Family IC Research Foundation and ICA Pilot Research Program
- Resources and publications for IC patients and their families plus a quarterly magazine, ICA Update
- Advocacy and disability support
- Referrals to doctors and healthcare providers with an expertise in IC
- Educational materials for healthcare provider resources, as well as a scientific newsletter, Professional Perspectives
- Monthly news bulletins via Café ICA

Interstitial Cystitis Network (ICN)
PO Box 2159,
Healdsburg CA 95448
Web address: www.ic-network.com
IC Shop Sales: 707-433-0413
Patient Help Line: 707-538-9442
Fax: 707-538-9444

ICN is a publishing company dedicated to interstitial cystitis and other pelvic pain disorders. They strive to present the world's best research, information, and support directly into the homes and offices of their users (patients, providers & IC researchers).

Highlights of the ICN website:
- A comprehensive online patient handbook, which outlines treatments, dietary concerns, research, physician locator, coping strategies, and more
- A free email magazine, and subscriber supported magazines and special reports
- An extraordinary message board system monitored by dozens of volunteers, dedicated to providing online emotional support and valid medical information regarding interstitial cystitis, treatments, and coping strategies
- The IC Shop and Market, offering food, supplement, and comfort products as well as resource publications
- Numerous resources for dietary modification including the "IC Chef" and "Fresh Tastes by Bev"
- "Meet the IC Expert" guest lectures given as online, moderated chats, with transcripts of lectures cataloged in the Patient Handbook

The Cystitis & Overactive Bladder Foundation (UK)
76 High Street,
Stony Stratford,
Buckinghamshire, United Kingdom MK11 1AH
Web address: www.cobfoundation.org
Phone: (UK number): +44 (0)1908 569169

The Cystitis and Overactive Bladder Foundation (COB) provides information and support to sufferers of bladder problems, including Interstitial Cystitis, Bacterial Cystitis and Overactive Bladder. COB is a charity that is financially supported by its members. The COB website has a resources section and a very popular message board system allowing patients to discuss conditions and support each other live online. In addition to providing information via their website, the COB Foundation also offers additional help to members via local groups and newsletters.

American Urological Association (Patient Information)
1000 Corporate Boulevard
Linthicum, MD 21090
Toll Free (U.S. only): 1-866-RING AUA (1-866-746-4282)
Phone: 410-689-3700
Web address: www.urologyhealth.org/index.cfm

UrologyHealth.org is a website for patients written and reviewed by expert urologists in partnership with the American Urological Association Foundation. Browse adult or pediatric conditions and even participate in educational webinars to learn more about urological conditions.

American Dietetic Association (ADA)
120 South Riverside Plaza, Suite 2000
Chicago, IL 60606-6995
Web address: www.eatright.org
Telephone: 800-877-1600

ADA is the world's largest organization of food and nutrition professionals, with more than 68,000 members. The ADA website has a search feature called "Find a Nutrition Professional" to help you locate a registered dietitian near you.

Other Websites

MayoClinic.com
www.mayoclinic.com

Mayo Clinic's three main web sites provide information and services from the world's first and largest integrated, not-for-profit group medical practice. View blogs, videos, slideshows and podcasts on countless health topics. Manage your health with information and tools that reflect the expertise of Mayo's 3,400 physicians and scientists, learn how to access medical services, and discover Mayo's medical research and education offerings.

WebMD
www.webmd.com

WebMD provides credible information, supportive communities, and in-depth reference material about health subjects. The WebMD content staff blends award-winning expertise in journalism, content creation, community services, expert commentary, and medical review to give their users a variety of ways to find what they are looking for.

urologychannel
www.urologychannel.com

Developed and monitored by board-certified physicians,
urologychannel provides comprehensive and trustworthy
information about urologic conditions. Urologychannel is a
medical information website of Healthcommunities.com, Inc.

Meals For You
www.mealsforyou.com

Meals For You is operated by Point of Choice, a leader in online
recipes and nutrition. The Meals For You website provides users
with recipes, meal plans, nutrition information, newsletters, and
shopping lists, using their proprietary database of over 10,000
recipes. *Meals For You* offers an "Advanced Search" option,
where a user can filter recipes by telling the search engine which
ingredients to avoid.

WeGoShop.com
www.wegoshop.com

WeGoShop.com is the largest, nationally expanding, full-service,
personalized grocery shopping and home delivery company in
the United States. By using the WeGoShop.com grocery delivery
service, you can avoid impulse shopping and unwanted trips to
fast food restaurants and convenience stores. There are
absolutely no mark-ups on your grocery items. You pay the same
amount that the grocery store of your choice charges for the
groceries you order, including sale and "club card" prices, plus
the modest grocery shopping and delivery charge.

National Institutes of Health: National Institute of Diabetes and Digestive Diseases and Kidney Diseases
http://kidney.niddk.nih.gov/kudiseases/pubs/interstitialcystitis

A US government sponsored website containing valuable information about diagnosis, causes, treatments, and research opportunities for interstitial cystitis.

Nutrition.gov
Web address: http://www.nutrition.gov

An extensive US government sponsored website providing nutrition information.

Information contained on Nutrition.gov:
- Dietary Supplements
- Diseases and Disorders
- Food Allergies
- Food Composition
- Food and Nutrition Assistance
- Food Safety
- Nutrition Recommendations
- Shopping, Cooking & Meal Planning
- Sports & Exercise
- Weight Control

US Department of Health and Human Services

National Institutes of Health

National Center for Complementary and Alternative Medicine

Web address: http://nccam.nih.gov/

The National Center for Complementary and Alternative Medicine (NCCAM) is one of the 27 institutes and centers that make up the National Institutes of Health (NIH). The NIH is one of eight agencies under the Public Health Service (PHS) in the Department of Health and Human Services (DHHS).

NCCAM is dedicated to exploring complementary and alternative healing practices in the context of rigorous science, training complementary and alternative medicine (CAM) researchers, and disseminating authoritative information to the public and professionals.

Quackwatch

Web address: http://www.quackwatch.com

Quackwatch is dedicated to providing balanced information and research on questionable complementary and alternative medicine (CAM) practices, aiding consumers as they make educated decisions about their health care.

Books

Confident Choices: Customizing the Interstitial Cystitis Diet
by Julie Beyer, MA, RD
Publisher: NutraConsults, LLC (2005)
ISBN: 0976724618

Confident Choices: Customizing the Interstitial Cystitis Diet is
an easy-to-use workbook that can help you determine your
personal food triggers and get you on your way to feeling better!
Bonus sections include information on nutrition supplements,
food intake and voiding diaries, and planning sheets. *Confident
Choices: Customizing the Interstitial Cystitis Diet* also includes
information on exercise, stress management, and emotional
issues, while illustrating success stories with patient stories.
Confident Choices: *Customizing the Interstitial Cystitis Diet* was
written by a registered dietitian who knows what it is like to live
with interstitial cystitis.

A Taste of the Good Life: A Cookbook for an Interstitial Cystitis Diet
by Beverley Laumann
Publisher: Freeman Family Trust Publications (July 1, 1998)
ISBN: 096657060X

A Taste of the Good Life is a wonderful reference on IC and diet, rich with recipes. It includes substitutions for people on multiple dietary restrictions.

The Interstitial Cystitis Survival Guide: Your Guide to the Latest Treatment Options and Coping Strategies
by Robert M. Moldwin
Publisher: New Harbinger Publications (October 30, 2000)
ISBN: 1572242108

Dr. Moldwin, a highly regarded urologist who specializes in IC, has taken the mystery out of IC diagnosis, treatments, and related conditions in this easy-to-read, comprehensive guide for physicians and patients about interstitial cystitis. This book includes a section dedicated to men who suffer from interstitial cystitis, a discussion of pelvic floor dysfunction, and even a chapter about pregnancy and IC.

***Patient to Patient: Managing Interstitial Cystitis and
Overlapping Conditions***
by Gaye Grissom Sandler, Andrew B. Sandler
Publisher: Bon Ange LLC; 1st edition (February 1, 2001)
ISBN: 0970559003

Patient to Patient is generously written from the hearts, minds,
education, and most of all, personal experiences of this husband
and wife team. Gaye, an IC patient and Aston-Patterning
movement and muscle re-education specialist, and Andrew, a
health administration expert with a degree in psychology, offer
patients their unique perspective when discussing common
problems that IC patients and their loved ones face on a daily
basis.

***A Headache in the Pelvis: A New Understanding and
Treatment for Prostatitis and Chronic Pelvic Pain Syndromes***
by David Wise
Publisher: National Center for Pelvic Pain; 3rd Rev Edition
(March 15, 2005)
ISBN: 0972775528

A Headache in the Pelvis describes the details of the Stanford
Protocol, a treatment for prostatitis and other chronic pelvic pain
syndromes that was developed at Stanford University Medical
Center in the Department of Urology. This book may be helpful
for both men and women who live with the frustrating and
sometimes disabling symptoms of pelvic dysfunction, such as
pain, difficulty with urination, or sexual problems.

When the Body Says No
by Gabor Mate
Publisher: Wiley; 1st edition (April 11, 2003)
ISBN: 0471219827

When the Body Says No carefully illustrates the connection between a person's health and their emotional state. Anyone who suffers from an autoimmune disease, an inflammatory condition, or cancer will find this book valuable. Gabor Mate develops a persuasive argument for the importance of understanding stress and its connection to disease.

Celebrate Life: New Attitudes for Living with Chronic Illness
by Kathleen Lewis, RN, MS, CMP, LPC
Publisher: Arthritis Foundation (October 25, 1999)
ISBN: 0912423242

Lewis, diagnosed with lupus, fibromyalgia, and osteoarthritis, is a medical psychotherapist and licensed counselor who celebrates her life with chronic illness and helps others do the same through her counseling services and writing. *Celebrate Life* provides a rich collection of strategies including how you can advocate for yourself with medical professionals, how to reward yourself, and how to find the way along the path to acceptance of living with chronic illnesses.

Food Allergy Survival Guide: Surviving and Thriving With Food Allergies and Sensitivities
by Vesanto Melina, Dina Aronson, Jo Stepaniak
Publisher: Healthy Living Publications (August 1, 2004)
ISBN: 157067163X

Enjoy life and food again. Written by three registered dietitians, *The Food Allergy Survival Guide* is yet another fantastic guide when dealing with food allergies and sensitivities. Readers can learn how food allergies and sensitivities affect their bodies, how to self-assess personal trigger foods without compromising nutrition, and learn how to find hidden sources of problem ingredients in their food. This book also contains vegetarian meal planning suggestions.

Nutritional Supplement Information

Information regarding these dietary supplements is taken directly from the individual company's marketing materials. Inclusion in this publication does not constitute endorsement, nor does exclusion from this list imply lack of endorsement.

Desert Harvest Aloe

1140 Amstel Drive
Colorado Springs, Colorado 80907
Toll Free: 800-222-3901
Fax: 719-598-8918
E-mail: support@desertharvest.com
Web address: http://www.desertharvest.com

Desert Harvest whole-leaf aloe vera capsules are very unique. Their aloe vera plants are grown organically, using no pesticides or chemical fertilizers. The leaves are harvested and cold processed to preserve the active ingredients. Desert Harvest does not use preservatives, artificial ingredients, or additives. The aloin and aloe emodin (chemicals that cause diarrhea) are removed using a patented formula. Aloe vera works as an antibiotic, pain reliever, and anti-inflammatory and promotes tissue regeneration.

Desert Harvest was the first aloe vera company that discovered the connection between whole leaf aloe and IC. They sponsored the first double-blind, placebo-controlled clinical trial of aloe vera use in IC patients, and have two more studies planned.

BladderQ and other supplements
The Natural Bladder
www.TheNaturalBladder.com
P.O. Box 5398
Glen Allen, VA 23058
800-566-5522
Email: helpdesk@thenaturalbladder.com

The Natural Bladder provides a variety of herbal remedies and natural products for overactive bladder, urinary tract infections, interstitial cystitis, and incontinence.

CystoProtek
Alaven Pharmaceutical LLC
2260 Northwest Parkway, Ste. D
Marietta, GA 30067
888-317-0001
Email: cystoprotek@alavenpharm.com

Alaven researchers have found that CystoProtek, a unique natural formula of chondroitin sulfate, glucosamine, quercetin, sodium hyaluronate and olive kernel extract, can help relieve many of the symptoms associated with cystitis and interstitial cystitis. CystoProtek has the anti-inflammatory power of chondroitin sulfate and quercetin but also includes glucosamine sulfate, and sodium hyaluronate to help heal the damaged bladder.

CystoProtek is the result of years of research into interstitial cystitis by Theoharis Theoharides, MD, PhD. Dr. Theoharides is a professor of Pharmacology, Internal Medicine and Bio Chemistry at Tuft's University in Boston. Alaven, LLC is a corporation dedicated to combining scientific investigation with natural healing. An outstanding team of prominent physicians and scientists from Ivy League universities form its advisory board.

CystaQ

Farr Laboratories
11100 Santa Monica Blvd. #560
Los Angeles, CA 90025
Toll Free: 877-284-3976
E-mail: service@cystaq.com
Web address: http://www.cystaq.com

CystaQ is a dietary supplement that was specifically developed to help patients with interstitial cystitis. CystaQ's ingredients include a proprietary formula of quercetin, bromalain, papain, cranberry powder, black cohosh (root) skullcap, wood betony (leaf), passionflower, and valerian.

Prelief

AkPharma Inc.
PO Box 111
Pleasantville, NJ 08232
Toll Free: 800-994-4711
E-mail: prbetty@akpharma.com
Web address: http://www.akpharma.com

Prelief is an acid reducer made from calcium glycerophosphate, a dietary supplement. IC patients have used Prelief successfully for years. In retrospective studies, Prelief helped to reduce bladder pain associated with consuming high acid foods in 70% of IC patients and reduced urinary frequency in over 60% of patients. Clinical studies are in progress to document Prelief's effectiveness.

pH Control

pH Sciences, Inc.
P.O. Box 65260
17230 12th Ave NE
Seattle, WA 98155
Fax: 206-364-5369
Email: info@phsciences.com
Web address: http://www.phsciences.com

The pH Control Alka-Plex compound is formed into a tablet specifically designed to pass through the stomach without dissolving. pH Control delivers an effective, natural, and safe acid neutralizer into the intestinal tract where it can be absorbed into the body fluids and be carried into the bladder and urinary tract. The effectiveness of pH Control has been proven in laboratory testing and pre-clinical studies. More studies are underway.

Index